THE HORSE
STRUCTURE AND MOVEMENT

THE HORSE

STRUCTURE AND MOVEMENT

by

R. H. SMYTHE
M. R. C. V. S.

Second Edition
Revised by
PETER C. GOODY, B.Sc. Ph.D. F.L.S.
Lecturer in Anatomy at the Royal Veterinary College

J. A. ALLEN & CO
LONDON

First published in 1967
by. J. ALLEN & CO
I LOWER GROSVENOR PLACE
LONDON, S.W.I

Second Edition (Revised) 1972

Printed and bound in England by
A. Wheaton & Co., Exeter

FOREWORD

This book has been written in response to a great many requests from judges and breeders of horses, owners and exhibitors, and from many who ride for pleasure. All desired to learn more about the framework of the body hidden beneath the skin and concerning the mechanism which propels the body. Most were anxious to discover what gave pattern to the various contours of the body and also what constituted good or bad conformation and whether good conformation implied good performance. The book has been written for the layman rather than for the veterinary surgeon who has studied anatomy in far greater detail than is needed in this volume; although some may possibly find something of interest in the sections dealing with movement.

The illustrations are all to be regarded as diagrammatic. They are intended to convey to the reader's mind in the simplest form some idea of the nature and relationship of parts of the body engaged in various gaits, especially in connection with galloping and jumping.

The book is written in sections rather than chapters, each fairly complete in itself. This entails some mild repetition but it enables each to be understood without undue reference to other sections. The appendix is selected from a series of articles published in *Horse and Hound* in 1965, reproduced by permission of the editor.

R. H. SMYTHE

PREFACE TO THE SECOND EDITION

This book was intended to be a simple guide to the structure of the horse and was written primarily for the layman rather than the veterinary surgeon. In undertaking the revision of the book I have tried to keep these original aims in mind. Thus the book is still presented in the same format of sections rather than chapters, each being fairly complete in itself. The first two sections dealing with the skeletal framework and the landmarks and surface markings of the body have been rearranged and rewritten. Also much additional information has been added, especially in section two, concerning the musculature involved in loco-motion. The third section, on movement, incorporates a considerable amount of extra material pertaining to the 'stay apparatus'. It also includes a more comprehensive statement concerning the musculature involved in locomotion. I hope that this section will now be of more use to those readers interested in the functional aspects of the musculoskeletal system. The section on conformation and the Appendix remain substantially un-changed. Throughout I have made changes in the nomenclature so that it now agrees with that used in standard anatomical texts such as Sisson and Grossman (The Anatomy of the Domestic Animals). However, where the name changed is one in normal veterinary useage it is placed in parentheses after the new name. I have also redrawn the illustrations with the assistance of Mrs. Shirley Fitzgerald of the Royal Veterinary College, but they still retain the diagrammatic nature of the original drawings. The photographs of the skeleton of Foxhunter (1940–1959) were taken by Mr. Stephen Barnett of the Royal Veterinary College to whom I extend my thanks. I am especially indebted to Mr. Frank Drury M.R.C.V.S. of the Royal Veterinary College for his advice and assistance in the preparation of this revision. Finally I hope that this revised edition will still serve the original purpose, but in addition will be of some interest to both veterinary student and veterinary surgeon.

P. C. GOODY

CONTENTS

Page

PART ONE

THE BONES OF THE HORSE 1

THE SKULL 1
Air spaces within the skull 6
Dentition 9

THE SPINE 13
The cervical vertebrae 13
Head movements 16
The thoracic vertebrae 16
The lumbar vertebrae 17
The sacrum 19
The coccygeal vertebrae 20
The vertebral column as a whole 20

THE RIBS AND STERNUM 22

THE FORELIMB 25
The scapula 26
The shoulder joint 29
The humerus 30
The radius and ulna 32
The elbow joint 34
The carpus or knee 35
Movements of the knee joint 36
The metacarpal bones 38
The phalanges 41
The sesamoid bones 46
The suspensory apparatus 47

THE HINDLIMB 49
The pelvic girdle 50
The hip joint 53

Page

The femur   55
The tibia and fibula   57
The stifle joint   59
Movement of the stifle joint   61
The tarsus or hock   63
Movement of the hock joint   66

PART TWO

THE SURFACE OF THE HORSE   69

THE SKIN   71
The skin musculature   72
The skin glands   73
The hair   74

THE HEAD   76
The nostrils and nasal cavity   81
The eyes and eyelids   82
The ears   84
The lips, mouth and tongue   85
The facial muscles   88
The intermandibular space   90

THE NECK AND POLL   91

THE FORELIMB   93
The shoulder   93
The forearm and knee   99
The metacarpus and digit   101

THE TRUNK   103

THE HINDLIMB   106
The hip, thigh and buttock   106
The leg and hock   109
The metatarsus and digit   112

Page

PART THREE

THE HORSE AT REST AND IN MOTION   113

Equilibrium and the centre of gravity   114
The horse at a standstill   116
Moving off   124
Coming to earth   131
The next step   133
On the way   137
Change of gait   138
Faster   139
And faster   142
A limit to speed   145
Coming to a halt   147
Jumping   148

PART FOUR

SOME THOUGHTS ABOUT CONFORMATION

    152

APPENDIX   160

The horse and how it works   160
Moving a rigid body   163
Swinging in a cradle   166
The vital hock   170
Occupational hazards   175
A glance at the foundations   180

ILLUSTRATIONS

PLATES
1. Skull and limb skeleton of Foxhunter   *facing page*   I
2. Skeleton of Foxhunter   *facing page*   160

CHARTS
1. The bones of the horse   *Page*   12
2. The surface of the horse   70
3. The superficial muscles of the horse   94

FIGURES
1. Skull of foal   *Page*   3
2. Skull in sagittal section   3
3. Skull for frontal sinuses   4
4. Skull for maxillary sinus   7
5. Incisor teeth   10
6. Hyoid apparatus   11
7. Cervical vertebrae   14
8. Ligamentum nuchae   15
9. Thoracic and lumbar vertebrae   17
10. Sacrum   19
11. Ribs and sternum   22
12. Scapula   27
13. Humerus   30
14. Radius and ulna   33
15. Elbow joint   34
16. Carpus   36
17. Carpus for ligaments   37
18. Metacarpus and digit   39
19. Limb below fetlock in sagittal section   42
20. Third phalanx   43
21. Suspensory apparatus   47
22. Pelvis and sacrum   51
23. Pelvis and ligaments   52
24. Hip joint   54
25. Femur   56
26. Tibia and fibula   58

27. Stifle joint   *Page*   60
28. Stifle joint   62
29. Tarsus   64
30. Tarsus   65
31. Variation in head shape   76
32. Landmarks on head and neck   78
33. Nasal cartilages   81
34. Head in sagittal section   86
35. Superficial muscles of the head   89
36. Deep muscles of the shoulder and arm   96
37. Muscles and tendons of the metacarpus and digit   100
38. Deep muscles of the hip and thigh   107
39. Muscles and tendons of the hock   110
40. Stay apparatus of the forelimb   118
41. Stay apparatus of the hindlimb   121
42. Gallop in greyhound and horse   164
43. Chest in section   167
44. Hock joint   172
45. Stifle joint and muscles operating the hock   174
46. Limb below fetlock in sagittal section   177
47. Passage of deep flexor tendon   178
48. Deep flexor tendon and distal sesamoid bone   178
49. Foot below pastern joint in sagittal section   181
50. Undersurface of the foot   182
51. Lateral cartilage of the third phalanx   183

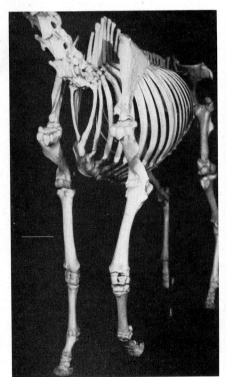

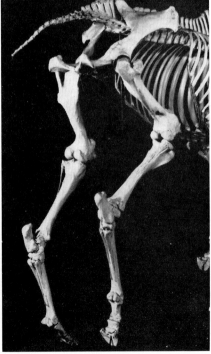

Plate 1. Skull, forelimbs and hindlimbs of Foxhunter (1940–1959) in the Anatomy
Department of the Royal Veterinary College, London.

PART ONE

THE BONES OF THE HORSE

A detailed study of the horse's skeleton would not only reveal the bones and their positions and relationships, but would necessitate a close examination of each separate bone with special regard to the many tuberosities and projections which disturb the contour of the body surface. These produce prominences and depressions and have a visible effect upon external appearance.

Bones carry projections and hollows for a variety of purposes. They may possess terminal enlargements in association with the formation of joints, or present surface projections for the attachment of muscles. Some bones, the skull and pelvic bones for example, may enclose and protect essential parts of the body such as the brain or the uterus. A great many bones, and especially their irregularities, may be palpated through the skin, and the following brief description and accompanying diagrams of the horse's bones may help to associate surface characteristics with the underlying bony structure.

THE SKULL

From a purely architectural standpoint the head of the horse at first sight is considerably more bulky than it need have been. However, much of the bulk and subsequent weight is associated with the teeth and jaws, and areas of bone associated with jaw muscle attachment. Thus it seems probable that the large size of the head is directly related to the feeding habits of the horse. It is also probable that the length of the neck is influenced to a large degree by the feeding habits. The horse is (or was) a grazing animal and in such animals it is a rule that the neck must be as long as the forelegs so that grass-cropping can be accomplished without undue inconvenience. Therefore the horse finds itself in the position of having a rather heavy head supported by a neck of some length. However, it can put these to good use as an oscillating

pendulum at the front end of the body enabling the horse to vary
the distribution of its body weight and maintain its balance both
when standing and moving, or even when the body is suspended
in mid-air while negotiating a jump. By raising or lowering the
head the horse is able to change the position of its centre of gravity.
While by moving it a little to one side or the other it can greatly
improve its chances of maintaining equilibrium, especially when
rounding corners at speed.

Of the numerous bones which enter into the making of the
skull those on the outside are mostly flattened and are united
along their edges during early life by cartilage which later becomes
replaced by bone. If the head of a dead foal is skinned, then boiled
until the flesh can be easily removed, all the bones become separated. If the proceeding is persisted in for some time the bones will
fall apart as the cartilage intervening between adjacent edges
disintegrates. When the foal grows into an adult the union
between the various bones of the skull gradually becomes firmer,
and by the eighth year the skull is solid and unyielding.

The two halves of the lower jaw become solidly united at the
mandibular symphysis (between the two central incisors, out of
the four present at this age) when the foal is only two months old.
Until this time the two halves of the jaw are separate. Similarly,
most long bones in the limbs carry articular portions (*epiphyses*)
at their extremities which are united only by cartilage to the main
shaft of the bone (*diaphysis*). The final solidification may not take
place until the colt or filly is approximately 2 years old, and in some
instances older.

The skull consists of two main portions, the *cranium* and *face*.
The former encloses the brain, the latter encloses oral and nasal
cavities. The division between the cranium and face may be
indicated approximately by a transverse plane through the front
border of the orbits (Fig. 1). In addition to these two parts the
tongue contains its own supporting bone, the hyoid apparatus,
made up of jointed sections (Fig. 6).

The *cranium* occupies the posterior one third of the skull and its
cavity is ovoid in shape. The roof is formed from the *supraoccipital*,
interparietal and *frontal* bones, the occipital being the strongest
and thickest. Damage to the horse's brain occurs more often,
curiously enough, at this upper part of the cranium where the

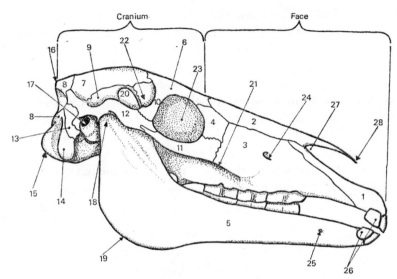

FIG. 1. Skull of foal in lateral view showing the sutures between separate bones. (1) Premaxilla. (2) Nasal. (3) Maxilla. (4) Lachrymal. (5) Mandible. (6) Frontal. (7) Parietal. (8) Occipital. (9) Squamous temporal. (10) Supraorbital process of the frontal. (11) Zygomatic process of the malar. (12) Zygomatic process of the temporal. (13) Mastoid process. (14) Paramastoid process. (15) Occipital condyle. (16) Nuchal crest. (17) External auditory meatus. (18) Mandibular condyle. (19) Angle of the mandible. (20) Coronoid process. (21) Facial crest. (22) Temporal fossa. (23) Orbit. (24) Infraorbital foramen. (25) Mental foramen. (26) Incisor teeth. (27) Nasomaxillary notch. (28) Nasal peak.

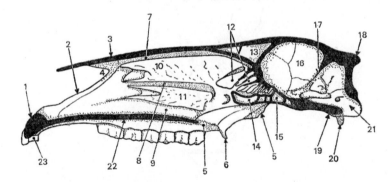

FIG. 2. Skull in sagittal section showing the interior of the nasal and cranial cavities. (1) Premaxilla. (2) Nasal process of the premaxilla. (3) Nasal. (4) Nasomaxillary notch. (5) Palatine. (6) Hamulus of the pterygoid. (7) Dorsal nasal meatus. (8) Middle nasal meatus. (9) Ventral nasal meatus. (10) Dorsal turbinate. (11) Ventral turbinate. (12) Ethmoturbinates. (13) Frontal sinus. (14) Palatine sinus. (15) Sphenoid sinus. (16) Cranial cavity. (17) Internal occipital protuberance. (18) External occipital protuberance. (19) Basal part of occipital. (20) Paramastoid process. (21) Foramen magnum. (22) Hard palate. (23) Incisor teeth.

T.H.—B

bone is thickest. The commonest cause is rearing up and falling backwards on to the occiput. This may cause fracture, not perhaps of the occiput itself, but of one of the smaller bones of the floor of the cranium.

Although the other bones of the cranial roof are thinner, the brain at the front is protected through being covered by the *frontal sinuses*, which provide a double roof of thin bone with a fairly voluminous air-space between them (Fig. 2). The most direct approach to the brain lies behind these in the triangle formed between the two temporal fossae, situated immediately behind the eye, and a point level with the bases of the ears where the

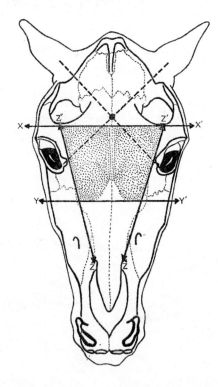

FIG. 3. Skull in dorsal view showing the position of the frontal sinuses. (After Taylor.) The sinuses are shown by stippling and can be mapped by constructing the following axes:

X—X' through the middle of the zygomatic arches; Y—Y' halfway between the inner angle of the eye and the end of the facial crest; Z—Z' from the nasomaxillary notch back through the inner angle of the eye. The point at which the broken lines cross indicates the position chosen for humane destruction, the lines being drawn from the inner angles of the eyes to the bases of the opposite ears.

skin beneath the forelock ends on the upper limit of the forehead. Beneath the skin covering this triangle only a relatively thin layer of bone protects the *cerebrum*, the major portion of the brain, apart from the covering of muscles overlying the cranial bones. This is the site chosen to carry out humane destruction of the animal (Fig. 3).

The rear end of the cranium is perforated by the *foramen magnum*, a large aperture through which the brain and spinal cord establish communication. The spinal cord travels down the back lying within the neural canal made up from a series of bony arches situated on top of the body of each of the bones forming the vertebral column.

Inside the skull the cranial cavity is partially divided into two compartments (Fig. 2). The anterior, larger compartment, contains the *cerebrum*, while the posterior one holds the *cerebellum* which is largely concerned with maintaining body balance (Fig. 34). Underlying the cerebellum is the *medulla*, the link between the brain and the spinal cord at the foramen magnum.

The outer surface of the anterior part of the cranium disappears at its lowest part into a cavity on either side known as the *orbital space* (Fig. 1). This contains the eyeball together with a quantity of semi-fluid fat amid which the eyeball is cradled. The front portion of the orbital space of the horse consists of a complete and prominent ring of bone. In some animals, such as the dog, the whole orbit is 'open', that is to say the portion containing the eyeball is continuous with the hinder part of the orbital space which contains the uppermost hind portion of the lower jaw (*coronoid process*). In the horse the orbit is 'closed' by means of a bony arch, the *supraorbital process*, which stretches across the orbital space from the frontal bone in the cranial roof to the zygomatic bone laterally. The supraorbital process can be located lying beneath the skin above the upper eyelid. This process is continuous below with a curved bar of bone known as the *zygomatic arch* which joins the *maxilla* in the lateral wall of the face with the *squamous temporal* bone in the lateral wall of the cranium. Between the arch and the lower part of the cranial wall is a space continuous in the prepared skull with the space containing the eye. This space is known as the *temporal fossa* and it houses the coronoid process of the lower jaw. It can be seen in the

living horse immediately behind the supraorbital process and it
is particularly noticeable at feeding time as the jaw movements
force fat from the orbital cavity into it as the mouth closes. In the
horse the fossa is comparatively small, admitting only the tip of
one finger, but in the dog, and other animals with open orbits,
the cavity is much greater.

The facial part of the skull forms the *nasal cavity* associated with
the sense of smell, and providing a passageway for respiratory
air-flow; and the *oral cavity* surrounded by upper and lower jaws.
The nasal cavity lies in front of the cranial cavity separated from
it by a transverse plate of bone (Fig. 2). The cavity is divided into
right and left halves by a mid-line, cartilaginous, *internasal septum*
which passes longitudinally down the entire cavity of the nose.
The olfactory sense is restricted to the nasal mucous membrane
covering a series of bony projections in the hindmost part of the
nasal chamber, the *ethmoid bones*. Projecting into the front part
of the nasal cavity from both sides are the *turbinate bones*, providing
an increased surface area for support of the highly vascular
mucous membrane of the nose (Figs. 2 and 34). Air circulating
through the spaces between the turbinates is warmed and moist-
ened before entering the lower respiratory passages. Whilst
examining the nasal cavities notice the considerable space
(*nasomaxillary notch*) between the pointed peak of the nasal bones
(Fig. 1) and the portion of the upper jaw beneath it. Observe
the amount of room left for the nasal passages.

AIR SPACES WITHIN THE SKULL
The comparatively large size of the head of the horse is due to the
fact that it requires considerable powers of mastication to enable it
to live. For this purpose it needs strong, continuously growing
cheek teeth, and large powerful jaws, which cannot be matched
up with a small cranium and light superstructures. So the upper
part of the skull requires enlargement in order to provide accommodation for adequate masticatory apparatus. This could be
achieved by merely increasing the surface area by new bone deposition. However, this would increase the weight of the head
too much. Therefore the enlarged bones include air cavities
within them, thus surface area is increased without any great
increase in volume, and subsequently weight, of the bone.

There are a number of such cavities in each half of the head; the *frontal*, *superior maxillary*, *inferior maxillary*, and *sphenopalatine sinuses*. The size and position of these can best be judged by reference to Figs. 2, 3 and 4. Briefly the frontal sinus is a large air space extending from the upper part of the nasal bones back to the level of the hind edge of the supraorbital process. The two halves, one on each side of the mid-line of the head, are completely separated by a thin bony partition. Each half communicates freely below

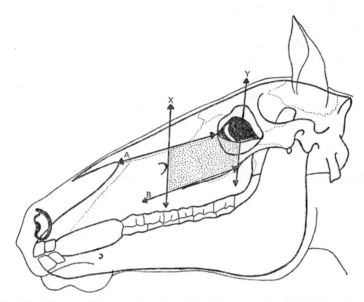

FIG. 4. Skull in lateral view showing the position of the maxillary sinus (After Taylor). The sinus is shown by stippling and can be mapped by constructing the following axes: X, vertically through the facial crest close to its front end; Y, vertically through the centre of the eye; A, from the nasomaxillary notch back through the inner angle of the eye; B, along the length of the facial crest, however, this lower limit varies with age and the degree of extrusion of the teeth.

with the large superior maxillary sinus placed on the same side of the head, extending beneath the orbit and along the area occupied by the molar teeth. The roots of the last three cheek teeth are lodged in the sinus invested in a thin layer of bone. The inferior maxillary sinus is smaller and completely separated from the superior sinus by a thin plate of bone, but both sinuses communicate directly with the nasal passage. The remaining sinus, the sphenopalatine sinus, is small but important. It lies below the ethmoid bones and is divided into a posterior *sphenoidal* and an anterior *palatine* part. The latter opens into the superior maxillary sinus. Infections of the first three sinuses may easily be drained by trephining. The sphenoidal part of the sphenopalatine sinus, having something of a blind end, is liable to retain infection as it is not easily amenable to surgical interference.

The sinuses fill, or at least change some part of their air content, during expiration. They are lined by a continuation of the mucous membrane of the nose and are readily involved in the course of nasal infections. In the horse at least they have no special function other than to provide the head with size and contour. They are not concerned with the sense of smell, the smell buds being confined to the mucosa covering the ethmoid bones.

An additional advantage gained from the frontal and superior maxillary sinuses is that, owing to their position, they push the orbits away from the central line of the head. Thus, instead of the horse possessing central vision with both eyes converging upon an object ahead, the eyes are placed somewhat laterally. In consequence of this the horse can see two pictures simultaneously, one with each eye, and can also see objects approaching from behind particularly if the body is streamlined without an excessively fat abdomen or very great width between the haunches. Although these abilities may not be especially useful to the horse in domestication, there is little doubt that they were of considerable advantage when the horse was hunted on open grassland by various carnivorous animals and badly needed to keep an eye on everything going on all around its body.

Returning again to the facial part of the skull and in particular the jaws. The *upper jaw* consists of *maxilla* and *premaxilla*, the former housing the upper cheek teeth, the latter supporting the upper incisors (Fig. 1). Both bones help to form the walls of the nasal cavity, and meet their fellows of the opposite side in the roof of the mouth where they form the *hard palate*. The *mandible* (lower jaw) is a very large structure housing the lower incisors and molars. The articulation between upper and lower jaws (*temporomandibular joint*) is seated beneath the posterior end of the zygomatic arch. Below and in front of the orbit the zygoma is continued forwards onto the maxillary surface as the *zygomatic ridge* or *facial crest*. This is designed to extend the area of origin of the powerful *masseter muscle* (the most important muscle employed in mastication), which is inserted into the flat roughened area on the outer face of the lower jaw. The other major masticatory muscle is the *temporal muscle* which extends from the upper surface of the cranium down into the temporal fossa to attach to the large coronoid process of the mandible.

The outer surface of the skull exhibits a number of small apertures (foramina) through which blood vessels and nerves pass. One large foramen in the maxillary bone is the *infraorbital foramen*, through which passes the large, sensory, infraorbital nerve to the nostrils and upper lip. A further foramen, the *supraorbital foramen*, is smaller and perforates the supraorbital process of the frontal bone above the eye. It also transmits a sensory nerve to the skin covering the forehead.

DENTITION

The examination of the *teeth* up to a certain period of life is one of the best methods of determining age. In the adult horse the permanent set of teeth consists of three *incisors*, one *canine*, three *premolars* and three *molars*, on either side of each upper and lower jaw. The deciduous or milk teeth are smaller and fewer in number, the adult molars having no deciduous precursors.

At birth the foal (Fig. 1) carries three cheek teeth, all temporary premolars which later will be cast and replaced by permanent molars, and the central incisor teeth. At 1 year old it has four cheek teeth, three premolars and the first permanent molar, and a full complement of deciduous incisors. At 4–5 years old it will have all six cheek teeth, the three permanent premolars and three permanent molars, and the deciduous incisors will have been replaced by permanent incisors. The ages at which the incisors appear and are fully developed in each jaw may be best shown as follows:

Central incisors	*Lateral incisors*	*Corner incisors*
Cut at $2\frac{1}{2}$ years,	Cut at $3\frac{1}{2}$ years,	Cut at $4\frac{1}{2}$ years,
up at 3 years	up at 4 years	up at 5 years

A supernumary premolar, the so-called *wolf tooth*, may appear in front of the first premolar at 5–6 months. The *tushes* or canine teeth are usually present in the male though small rudimentary tushes are quite common in mares. They appear at $3\frac{1}{2}$–4 years and are fully developed at $4\frac{1}{2}$–5 years, being absent in a 2 year old.

From 5 years old onwards age may be determined by the shape of the *tables* (masticatory surfaces) of the incisor teeth and by the amount of wear as shown by the depth and appearance of the grooves normally present on the tooth tables, the parts where

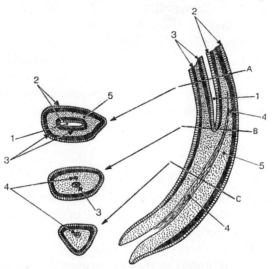

FIG. 5. Incisor tooth in long section and in cross section at the three levels A, B and C (After Taylor). These sections show how the shape of the tooth varies as it approaches the root, and also how the structure of the tooth table changes in accordance with the stage of wear of the crown.

(1) Infundibulum.   (2) Cement.   (3) Enamel.   (4) Pulp cavity containing new dentine.   (5) Dentine.

wear takes place. Teeth wear down from *crown* to *root*; at the same time they are being pushed out of the *alveolus* (socket) by growth of the root. An outer *enamel* layer covers a layer of *dentine* and also lines the central depression (*infundibulum*). As wear takes place the enamel is presented on the tooth table in a definite pattern (Fig. 5).

At 6 years old, in a well formed mouth, the upper and lower incisors meet at a right angle with no forward inclination. After 6 years they commence to incline in a forward direction until at 20 years they meet at an acute angle.

Notches make their appearance in the outer edges of the upper corner incisor teeth at certain ages. A notch appears at the posterior angle of the biting surface of the corner incisor tooth at 7 years, and as a result a projection develops at its posterior edge. It disappears soon after 8 years, and reappears at 11 years to persist usually throughout life. At 10 years *Galvayne's groove*, a longitudinal furrow often darkly stained, first appears at the outer portion of each corner incisor adjacent to the gum. By 15 years it has reached halfway down the tooth and attained its lower edge, the biting surface, at 20 years. After this it commences to disappear from above downwards at the same rate at which it made its appearance.

Before we leave the skull we must mention the *hyoid apparatus* at the base of the tongue (Fig. 6). This consists of a pair of *great cornua* connected above with the *hyoid processes of the petrous temporal bones* on the underside of the skull. Below the great cornua are

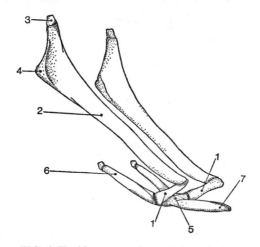

FIG. 6. Hyoid apparatus in anterolateral view.
(1) Small cornu. (2) Great cornu. (3) Articular cartilage of great cornu. (4) Muscular angle of great cornu. (5) Body of hyoid. (6) Thyroid cornu. (7) Lingual process.

attached to the transversely oriented *hyoid body* through the *small cornua*. The whole apparatus resembles a childs swing with the body of the hyoid being the seat. The body is also joined up with the *thyroid cartilage* of the larynx through the medium of the *thyroid cornua*. The *lingual process* projects forwards from the hyoid body and is buried in the root of the tongue. The hyoid apparatus therefore serves as an important area for attachment of tongue, pharyngeal and laryngeal muscles, and also serves to suspend the larynx in the ventral part of the throat.

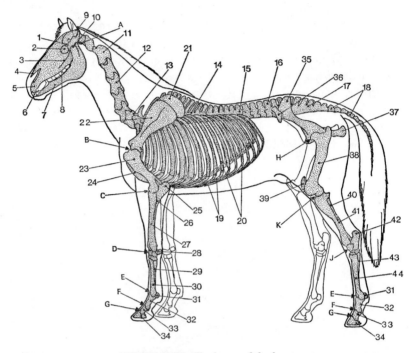

CHART ONE. The bones of the horse.

(1) Supraorbital process. (2) Orbit. (3) Facial crest. (4) Nasal peak. (5) Premaxilla. (6) Incisor teeth. (7) Lower jaw. (8) Cheek teeth (molars and premolars). (9) Nuchal crest. (10) Atlas. (11) Axis. (12) Fourth cervical vertebra. (13) Seventh cervical vertebra. (14) Ninth thoracic vertebra. (15) Last thoracic vertebra. (16) Fourth lumbar vertebra. (17) Sacrum. (18) Coccygeal vertebrae. (19) Costal cartilages. (20) Ribs. (21) Cartilage of prolongation of scapula. (22) Scapula. (23) Humerus. (24) Sternum. (25) Olecranon process. (26) Ulna. (27) Radius. (28) Accessory carpal. (29) Small metacarpal. (30) Large metacarpal. (31) Proximal sesamoid. (32) First phalanx. (33) Second phalanx. (34) Third phalanx. (35) Tuber sacrale. (36) Tuber coxae. (37) Tuber ischii. (38) Femur. (39) Patella. (40) Fibula. (41) Tibia. (42) Tuber calcis. (43) Small metatarsal. (44) Large metatarsal. (A) Jaw or temporomandibular joint. (B) Shoulder joint. (C) Elbow joint. (D) Knee joint. (E) Fetlock joint. (F) Pastern joint. (G) Coffin joint. (H) Hip joint. (J) Hock joint. (K) Stifle joint.

THE SPINE

The spine or *vertebral column* consists of seven *cervical* (neck) *vertebrae*; eighteen *thoracic* (dorsal) *vertebrae* each of which carries a pair of ribs; six *lumbar vertebrae*; a *sacrum* made up of five bones fused together by ossification of the cartilaginous material which united them during foetal life; and approximately eighteen *coccygeal* (tail) *vertebrae* (Chart One). The vertebrae have a common structural plan, being built from three basic components, *body*, *arch* and *processes*. These components have different fates in the various parts of the spine.

THE CERVICAL VERTEBRAE

The first two neck bones (Fig. 7) are different structurally from the others and from each other. The *vertebral canal*, through which the spinal cord passes, is of greater diameter in these than in the other vertebrae, a precaution against damage to the cord at a site where there is a great deal of movement. The first cervical bone, the *atlas*, lacks a body which is present in all the others, being a ring or short tube carrying on either side a considerable plate of bone termed the *wing*. The whole vertebra is arranged somewhat after the manner of a tortoise shell. Two large concave articular facets are present on the front of the atlas for receiving the *occipital condyles* of the skull.

The second cervical bone, the *axis*, has two peculiarities. Firstly it bears at the front end of its body a tooth-like projection, the *odontoid process*, which extends forwards into the lower part of the ring formed by the atlas. The upper surface of the odontoid process is roughened to provide attachment for a strong transverse ligament which unites it to the atlas and keeps the process securely retained within the lower part of the ring of the atlas. The process has articular facets on each side of it, and another below it, which form joints with the hinder end of the atlas. The second peculiarity of the axis is that it carries a surprisingly massive and strong dorsal spinous process. This is thickened and divided longitudinally along its upper edge into two ridges which diverge posteriorly. Dorsal neck musculature attaches to these ridges but, more importantly, attachment is given to a portion of the *ligamentum nuchae*, the strong central ligament of the neck

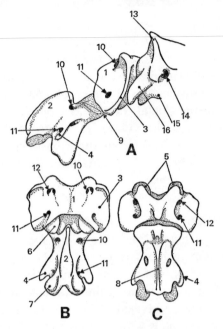

FIG. 7. First two cervical vertebrae (atlas and axis).
A. Lateral view.   B. Dorsal view.   C. Ventral view.
(1) Dorsal arch of the atlas.   (2) Spinous process of the axis.   (3) Wing of the atlas.
(4) Transverse process of the axis.   (5) Anterior articular cavities of the atlas.   (6)
Anterior articular process of the axis.   (7) Posterior articular process of the axis.
(8) Ventral spine of the axis.   (9) Odontoid process of the axis.   (10) Intervertebral
foramina.   (11) Transverse foramina.   (12) Alar foramen.   (13) Nuchal crest.
(14) External auditory meatus.   (15) Basal part of occipital.   (16) Paramastoid
process.

(Fig. 8). This nuchal ligament is made up of two parts:

(1) a rope-like *funicular portion* which passes forwards from the
highest dorsal spines in the region of the withers over the top of
the spinous process of the axis to become attached finally to the
nuchal crest of the occiput of the skull;

(2) a *lamellar portion* which lies in the middle of the neck and throws
out branches in fan-like formation, attached at their upper ends
to the underside of the funicular portion and radiating downwards
to insert onto the cervical vertebrae.

The ligament helps to hold up the head and neck, and, being
elastic, it also permits the head to be raised and lowered by
gravity and by means of the neck muscles. The funicular portion
is best viewed as a continuation forwards of the *supraspinous liga-*

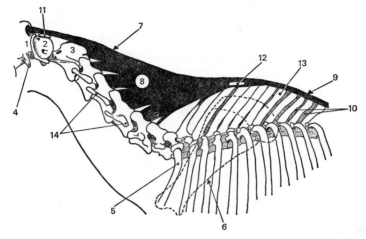

FIG. 8. Ligamentum nuchae and its relationships to the cervical and thoracic vertebrae
(After Nickel, Schummer and Seiferle).
(1) Rear end of skull. (2) Atlas. (3) Axis. (4) Paramastoid process. (5) First rib.
(6) Outline of scapula. (7) Funicular portion of ligament. (8) Lamellar portion of
ligament. (9) Supraspinous ligament. (10) Interspinous ligaments. (11) Atlantal
bursa. (12) Supraspinous bursa. (13) Seventh thoracic spine. (14) Transverse
process of cervical vertebra.

ment which extends along the back from the sacrum attaching to
the tops of all the spinous processes of lumbar and thoracic vertebrae en route.

Two *synovial bursae* are associated with the funicular part of
the ligament. The *atlantal bursa* lies between the ligament and the
arch of the atlas; the *supraspinous bursa* lies over the second thoracic
spine. Without going into any details of structure we may simply
say that synovial bursae are sacs containing synovial fluid which
are interposed at points of unusual pressure between a tendon,
ligament or muscle and some underlying structure, usually a
skeletal prominence. They facilitate tendon movement and provide
some measure of protection through their cushioning effect.

The remaining five cervical vertebrae conform more to the
normal vertebral plan with a body surmounted by an arch which
surrounds the vertebral canal. The arch supports a low dorsal
spinous process and a pair of articular processes both fore and
aft. Of particular interest are the transverese processes which are
prominent and plate-like. These project laterally and have
thickened roughened edges which serve for muscle attachment,

in particular the cervical part of the serratus ventralis muscle (Fig. 38). In a horse in good condition the lateral surfaces of the *transverse processes* of the cervical vertebrae can be palpated deeply through the overlying musculature on the lateral surface of the neck.

HEAD MOVEMENTS

The joint between the occipital bone of the skull and the first cervical bone, the atlas, permits nodding (up and down) movements of the head upon the neck. That between the atlas and axis permits, within limits, rotation of the head upon the neck, i.e. the atlas carrying the skull pivots on the odontoid process through a longitudinal axis. The joints between the last five cervical vertebrae allow lateral movements of the neck, lateral curvature, together with some degree of arching of the neck in which convexity of the spinal bones is directed upwards. Movements to produce the opposite condition in which the convexity is increased in a downward direction can only be very limited.

THE THORACIC VERTEBRAE

Being typical vertebrae the thoracics will serve to demonstrate how neighbouring bones of the spine are linked together. They also have additional articular surfaces to accommodate the heads of the ribs. The vertebral bodies are short as compared with those of the cervical bones, but like them are united by intervertebral cartilaginous substance, the so-called 'discs'.

At each side of the articular end of the body, before and behind, is a little concave articular surface termed the *costal facet* (Fig. 9). In this way between each pair of thoracic vertebrae there is provided, on either side, a cup-shaped cavity for articulation with the head (*capitulum*) of a rib. Transverse processes project from the vertebral arch on either side each carrying a smooth articular surface which articulates with the *tuberculum* of the rib.

The *articular processes* common to vertebrae in general are present but smaller than in the cervical vertebrae. The paired anterior processes articulate with the paired posterior processes of the adjacent vertebra.

The *spinous processes* are of great size in the early thoracic vertebrae reaching their maximum height at the fourth and

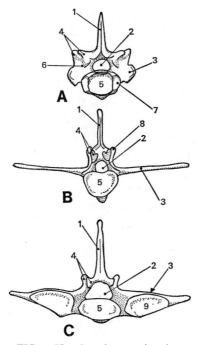

FIG. 9. Vertebrae in posterior view.
A. First thoracic. B. First lumbar. C. Last lumbar.
(1) Spinous process. (2) Vertebral canal. (3) Transverse process. (4) Articular processes. (5) Body. (6) Arch. (7) Rib facet. (8) Mamillary process. (9) Articular facet for sacral wing.

diminishing to the fifteenth or sixteenth (the *anticlinal* or *diaphragmatic vertebra*). The first fifteen spines point backwards, the anticlinal vertebra is vertical, the last two thoracic vertebral spines incline forwards (Chart One). Out of the eighteen thoracic bones the first seven lie partly behind the sloping scapula, which also covers the heads of the third to seventh ribs. There is very limited movement in the thoracic part of the spine of the horse in any direction.

THE LUMBAR VERTEBRAE
There are usually six lumbar bones, but occasionally only five are present. In this latter situation an extra thoracic vertebra occurs and is found especially in eastern breeds such as the Arab. The lumbar vertebrae are remarkable for the length and width of their transverse processes which project at almost right angles

from their bodies (Fig. 9). Each may be 3–4 inches in length and an inch in width. The lumbar bones of the horse differ from those of other animals since the lateral processes of the last three carry extra articular facets one on each side of the cartilaginous union between the bodies of these bones. These facets are present only on the hinder edge in the case of the fourth lumbar bone, but they are also present on the leading edge of the first of the fused sacral bones (Fig. 10). This ensures that the last three lumbar vertebrae and the sacrum are united by true *synovial joints* on their transverse processes and by cartilage 'glueing' together their bodies. This suggests that in the region of the loins the vertebral column has a strictly defined and very limited degree of movement, the part where one might expect a good deal of movement. The fact is that the spine of the horse exhibits little movement apart from that in the neck and tail. The very limited movement that does occur in the thoracolumbar region is found between the last thoracic and first lumbar bone, between the first three lumbar bones, and some strictly limited movement between the hinder lumbar vertebrae. This movement is necessarily very slight and any degree of movement between such bones must be dependent to a great extent upon the thickness of the cartilaginous intervertebral discs. These are firmly united to the bodies of the vertebrae so much so that one might regard intervertebral cartilages as portions of the bodies of the bones which have not yet become calcified. The words 'not yet' refer to the fact that with advanced years calcification between adjoining vertebrae is quite common in the horse and very frequently further outgrowths of bone act as 'bridges' across neighbouring bones making their union more complete. In the case of the synovial articulations between the transverse processes of the last three lumbar bones an active arthritis may occur as early as the second or third year in one or more of these articulations, terminating in solid fusion, often with the formation of a good deal of fresh bony deposit surrounding the actual joints. The lumbosacral joint is not normally included in this ankylosis. Examination of the skeleton of horses of all ages indicates that fusion is the rule rather than the exception. Unfortunately perhaps the extent of fusion and its rate of progress is not always general, so that two adjacent lumbar vertebrae may be united by the transverse processes on one side and unattached on the other. This condition may be conducive to pain and impaired efficiency in horses expected to race, hunt or jump. However, it is possible that most of these cases recover their efficiency when fusion finally takes place.

THE SACRUM

This composite bone lying beneath the loins in the region of the croup is composed of five vertebrae fused firmly together (Fig. 10). Sometimes the first of the tail vertebrae will be found solidly fused to the hindmost bone of the sacrum giving the impression that it

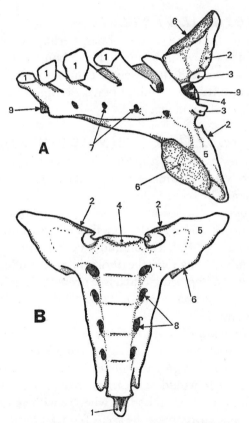

FIG. 10. Sacrum showing the five fused vertebrae.
A. Dorsolateral view. B. Ventral view.
(1) Spinous processes. (2) Articular facets for articulation with the last lumbar vertebra. (3) Articular processes. (4) Body. (5) Sacral wing. (6) Auricular surface which forms sacroiliac joint. (7) Dorsal sacral foramina. (8) Ventral sacral foramina. (9) Sacral part of vertebral canal.

contains six bones instead of five. The sacrum is triangular in form and it lies in the roof of the pelvic cavity with its posterior end a little higher than its anterior end.

The pelvic bones representing, through the ilia, the upper extremity of the hindlimbs are united to the sacrum on either side by the apposition of their somewhat roughened auricular surfaces. These are not united by a typical synovial joint but by means of an interosseous ligament composed of short, strong, white fibres, the *sacroiliac ligament* which divides the articulation up into a series of small synovial joints.

THE COCCYGEAL VERTEBRAE

There are usually eighteen tail bones, perhaps one more or less at times, which follow the sacrum. These bones begin to lose their articular processes and their neural canals after the third coccygeal vertebra, until the terminal bones become merely short rods united by discs of cartilage.

THE VERTEBRAL COLUMN AS A WHOLE

The total length of the horse's spine presents a succession of curves when viewed from the side (Chart One). It is slightly arched (concave below) at the upper end of the neck, but becomes concave above in the lower third of the neck and just before it joins the thoracic spine. At the junction of neck and thorax there is a marked change of direction and a very gentle curve, concave below, extends throughout the thoracic and lumbar regions. It should be noticed in passing that a line drawn through the summits of the spinous processes does not correspond to the curves formed by the vertebral bodies.

The slightly ventrally concave bow of the thoracolumbar region provides a static advantage in supporting the body weight. If the column were straight, or convex beneath, the body weight acting downwards would tend to decrease the area of contact between adjacent vertebral bodies, whereas with ventral concavity body weight tends to increase the area of contact between vertebrae. The dorsal spines of the thorax are bound in a row by strong ligaments and each neighbouring pair of bones is firmly united the one with the other through the articular processes aided by a number of closely binding ligaments. It follows therefore, that while the neck bones are freely movable the thoracic bones form an almost rigid column.

The situation in the lumbar spine has already been discussed, and it would seem that, apart from the neck, any degree of spinal flexion will be present between the last thoracic and first lumbar vertebra, between the first three lumbar bones, and at the lumbo-sacral junction. The vertebral column, being the axis upon which the limbs act to produce movement, will be flexed at these areas by forces produced by the pushing back of the hindlimbs against the ground. Both oblique and vertical forces are exerted on the spine by the hindlimbs. Oblique forces are exhibited as a tendency to flex the spine sideways, while vertical forces tend to increase the curvature of the thoracolumbar bow, i.e. to flex the spine vertically. Sideways forces and the resultant lateral oscillation are clearly apparent at the walk. At speeds higher than the walk muscular resistance increases making the column as rigid as possible in order to eliminate wasteful sideways movements. Vertical forces tending to increase the curvature of the spine are actively resisted and straightening of the thoracolumbar bow adds significantly to the forward propulsive thrust. Above the spinal cord the *longissimus dorsi muscle* as one example, and below it the *psoas minor muscle* as another, cooperate by simultaneous contraction in an effort to counter attempts on the part of the horse to flex its spine. When the synchronization between these muscles fails to operate, as during a fall or sometimes when galloping on level ground, and especially when laid out on the ground with limbs tied together in the early stages of anaesthesia, fracture of the back may occur. The damage usually takes place at its most rigid portion, which is generally somewhere in the thoracic region.

The calibre of the *vertebral canal*, the channel above the body of each vertebra through which the spinal cord passes giving out nerve trunks as it travels backward along the body, varies in different regions. This feature is designed in order to give the spinal cord full protection. As noticed earlier the calibre is greatest in the atlas, the first cervical vertebra. It diminishes considerably until the canal traverses the last three cervical and first two thoracic vertebrae where it becomes a great deal larger to accommodate the cervical enlargement of the cord. After this it narrows again until it reaches a minimum in the middle of the back. It increases again in the lumbar vertebrae at the lumbar enlargement, until the last or second last, when the calibre diminishes until the canal disappears at about the fourth coccygeal vertebra. The spinal cord actually comes to an end in the middle of the sacrum giving off coccygeal nerves which extend back in the spinal canal for a considerable distance and which supply the tail.

THE RIBS AND STERNUM

There are normally eighteen pairs of *ribs*, each thoracic vertebra carrying a rib on either side or, better perhaps, one pair of ribs

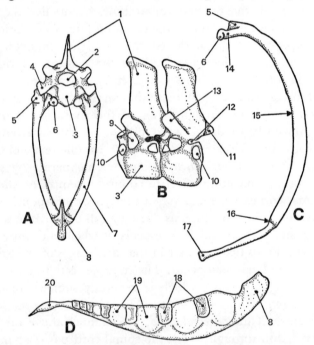

FIG. 11. Thoracic rib-cage components.
A. First thoracic vertebra with first ribs, anterior view. B. Fifteenth and sixteenth thoracic vertebrae, lateral view. C. Eighth rib, anterior view. D. Sternum showing its segmented nature, lateral view.
(1) Spinous processes. (2) Vertebral canal. (3) Body. (4) Transverse process. (5) Tubercle of rib. (6) Head (capitulum) of rib. (7) First rib. (8) Cariniform cartilage of sternum. (9) Tubercular facet. (10) Capitular facet. (11) Articular process. (12) Intervertebral foramen. (13) Mamillary process. (14) Neck of rib. (15) Eighth rib. (16) Costochondral junction. (17) Costal cartilage. (18) Costal facets. (19) Sternebrae. (20) Xiphoid cartilage.

with their heads fitted in between each pair of thoracic bones (Fig. 11).

A rib is an elongated, curved and highly elastic bone. At its lower end it carries a prolongation in the form of a rod of cartilage the *costal cartilage*. The first eight pairs of ribs articulate through their costal cartilages with the sides of the *sternum*, the breastbone, and are termed *sternal ribs*. The last ten pairs of ribs do not do this. These *asternal ribs* have their cartilaginous costal prolongations bound together, each being attached for nearly its whole length to its predecessor in the series forming the *costal arch* (Chart One). In young horses the rib cartilages are soft and gristly in nature, but in old horses they become calcified and solid. The first rib (Fig. 11A) is short and the least curved. The degree of curvature increases up to the last, the cartilage of which is not attached to the one in front of it, but projects freely into the abdominal wall. This last rib is short and termed the 'floating rib'.

Between and overlying the ribs are muscles which cause them to rotate in a forward and outward direction to induce inspiration (Chart Three and Fig. 36). Owing to the curvature of the ribs the chest capacity is thus increased and inspiration occurs as air is drawn into the lungs. When the ribs rotate in the opposite direction to lie flat against the chest wall air is forced out of the lungs. Between the serous membrane (*parietal pleura*) lining the inside of the chest wall, and that covering the lungs (*visceral pleura*), there is a potential cavity containing a vacuum. The two layers of pleura are kept in close apposition by a thin fluid film, so that the lungs dilate and contract in accordance with the movements of the chest wall.

The first rib, although the smallest, is especially important since it carries on its anterior edge grooves which are imprints of the nerves of the *brachial plexus*, a collection of large nerve trunks which supply locomotory and sensory impulses to the forelimb. If the first rib is broken, as not infrequently happens during accidents or falls, the resulting swelling may put pressure upon some of the nerves passing around the first rib with resulting muscular paralysis and skin desensitisation. The commonest type is *radial paralysis*, the radial nerve supplying the extensor muscles below the shoulder. In such a situation the horse cannot bring the lower part of the limb forward and so the knee remains flexed and the foot drags along the ground upon the toe. At the same time the elbow, lacking muscular support, drops down several inches below its normal position. Radial paralysis is therefore often termed 'dropped elbow'.

One last factor concerning the ribs is of importance, this being that the lateral surfaces of the first nine ribs give origin to the thoracic part of the *serratus ventralis* muscle (Fig. 36). The cervical part of this muscle we have already noticed as having an origin from the transverse processes of the last five cervical vertebrae. The two parts together form a large fan of muscle on the lateral surface of the thorax and neck which converges dorsally onto the inner face of the scapula (Fig. 34). The significance of this muscle will become apparent later in Part Three.

The *sternum* or breastbone forms the floor of the thorax or chest, and is held in position by the first eight pairs of ribs, the lower ends of which join up with it on either side at regular intervals by means of their costal cartilages (Fig. 11). In the horse the sternum is long, narrow and canoe-shaped but is not actually a single bone. It is made up of a number of distinct bony segments connected by intervening cartilage in the young subject, a great deal of the cartilage remaining throughout life. The sternum and costal cartilages of the ribs give extensive origin to the series of *pectoral* muscles which pass outwards to attachment areas on the fascia of the arm and the shaft of the humerus. One important component the *anterior deep pectoral* muscle passes up around the front of the shoulder to an insertion on the prescapular fascia. Like the ventral serrate muscle the importance of this muscle will be explained in Part Three.

In front the sternum carries the *presternal* or *carinform cartilage* which gives attachment to some of the neck muscles, e.g. the sternocephalic muscle which forms the lower border of the jugular furrow and attaches to the mandibular ramus. The hinder end of the sternum is drawn out into a flat, heart-shaped *xiphoid cartilage* which forms the floor at the front end of the abdomen and gives attachment to the sternal muscle fibres of the *diaphragm*, the muscular partition between thorax and abdomen. The remainder of the diaphragmatic musculature arises from the costal arch and the undersides of the lumbar vertebrae.

THE FORELIMB

The first thing one must understand about the forelimb of the horse is that it is not attached to the body by bone, not in fact by anything firmer and harder than muscle and ligamentous material. The horse has no *clavicle* (collar bone) and it would be possible to remove the forelimb from the carcass of a horse using nothing more than a knife. One advantage of this is that the muscles holding limb and body together, plus the cooperative antagonism of extensor and flexor muscles within the limb, are able to absorb a great deal of concussive force which would be transmitted up the limb and so to the spine if the limb were more solidly united to the body.

From above to below the bones of the forelimb are:

(a) the *scapula* or *bladebone*;

(b) the *humerus* or *armbone*, reaching from shoulder to elbow;

(c) the *radius* and *ulna*, extending from elbow to knee (these two bones are fused together in the horse);

(d) the *carpus* or *knee*, made up of seven bones most of which are flattened and fitted with wide, smooth articular surfaces;

(e) the *metacarpal bones*, only one of which is fully functional (the small metacarpals on either side merely help to support some of the knee bones and represent the remains of the other two digits horses possessed in the days when they were swamp dwellers);

(f) the *phalanges*, of which there are three in the modern soliped horse;

  (i) single, undivided *first phalanx* (long pastern or os suffraginis);

  (ii) shorter *second phalanx* (short pastern or os coronae) lying partly inside the hoof and partly above it at the coronet;

  (iii) *third phalanx* (pedal bone or os pedis) lying entirely within the hoof.

The third phalanx is attached to the inner surface of the hoof by means of a great number of flat leaves, the *sensitive laminae*, arising from its outer covering the *corium*. These sensitive laminae are interposed between similar *horny* (*insensitive*) *laminae* projecting in from the inner surface of the horny wall of the hoof. The solar surface of the third phalanx is united to the horny sole below it by means of numerous papillae which fit into small pores (tubules) on the inner surface of the sole.

In front the sole of the hoof presents a rounded or convex border by which it is intimately connected with the lower border of the wall of the hoof. In the clean, unshod foot this line of union is quite visible just inside the inner margin of the wall (Fig. 50 in the Appendix). At the hinder part of the sole it can be seen to turn inwards and then forwards to form an inner lining to the bars. It is known as the *white line*. When nailing on a shoe it is important that the nail neither punctures this division between horny and sensitive parts of the foot, nor presses unduly upon it to cause 'nail-binding'.

The structure of the foot will be considered in more detail later on, but for the moment it is only necessary to understand the manner in which the third phalanx is intimately connected with the hoof structure in order to establish a working connection between forelimb and ground.

THE SCAPULA

This bone is a triangular, flattened plate (Fig. 12) serving to attach the forelimb to the trunk by means of muscles and ligaments. It partially covers, from the lateral aspect, the first six or seven ribs from which it is separated by muscles underlying it and also by a lot of loose connective tissue (reminiscent in some ways of foam rubber). This connective tissue permits the scapula to move freely over the underlying ribs when pulled in one direction or another by muscles attached to its surfaces and borders.

Although this will become more apparent later, it may be noted at this point that the thorax is actually slung up between the two scapulae through the *serratus ventralis* muscles, one on either side of it. This means that just as the scapulae can glide upon the ribs so the trunk can move about between the scapulae (Fig. 43 in the Appendix). This degree of movement is brought about by uni-lateral contraction of the *serratus ventralis, anterior deep pectoral, rhomboideus* and *trapezius* muscles, all having attachments to the scapulae. Weight is shifted to the limb on the side of the muscles acting, and this is of great importance in maintaining balance especially when cornering at speed and when moving over uneven ground. It is this which enables a polo pony or a

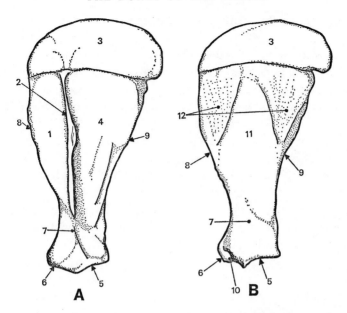

FIG. 12. Scapula of the left side in lateral view (A). Scapula of the right side in medial view (B).
(1) Supraspinous fossa. (2) Scapular spine. (3) Cartilage of prolongation. (4) Infraspinous fossa. (5) Glenoid fossa. (6) Scapular tuberosity. (7) Neck. (8) Anterior border. (9) Posterior border. (10) Coracoid process. (11) Subscapular fossa. (12) Serrated face of scapula.

'cutting horse' to carry out rapid bending movements. We must bear in mind that the horse is an animal with an almost rigid spine, and the freedom of movement attained by slinging the thorax between the two scapulae has been a significant factor in the evolution of the modern horse. Indeed, it made the horse a match for the carnivorous animals which possessed flexible spines and were able to develop great speeds over short distances (Fig. 42 in the Appendix).

The outer surface of the scapula is triangular with the base uppermost. It is divided longitudinally by a prominent *scapular spine* which cuts it into two sections of which the posterior is the wider. The two cavities thus formed are filled by muscle, the supraspinatus muscle in front and the infraspinatus muscle behind. These muscles are quite visible through the skin and between them the spine of the scapula can be felt with the fingers. The supraspinatus can extend the shoulder joint thus advancing the limb generally, while the infraspinatus can rotate the fore-limb in an outward direction. As well as separating the two spinatus muscles the scapular spine serves for the insertion of the trapezius muscle as this extends down over the withers from an origin in the mid-dorsal line. It also serves for the origin of the deltoid muscle which crosses the outer surface of the shoulder joint to attach to the humerus (Chart Three).

The inner surface of the scapula is hollowed out along its length for the origin of the subscapular muscle, which is an adductor of the limb, i.e. a muscle preventing the limb from being pulled outwards away from the body.

The upper edge of the horse's scapula carries a crescent-shaped *cartilage of prolongation*, a part of the foetal scapula which has never undergone ossification. The inner surface of this cartilage gives attachment to the rhomboideus muscle (Fig. 36). This muscle anchors the scapula to the nuchal ligament and the front eight or nine thoracic spines. It pulls the upper end of the scapula forwards, as well as helping to rotate the thorax between the two limbs (Fig. 43 in the Appendix).

At its lower end the scapula tapers to a *neck* which carries a *glenoid cavity* for articulation with the head of the humerus. A projection known as the *scapular tuberosity* lies in front of the glenoid surface occupying a very exposed spot close to the point of the shoulder where injury from contusion, especially among hunters and jumpers, may occur. This tuberosity gives origin to the biceps brachii muscle which is a shoulder extensor (also an elbow flexor). Between the tendon of this muscle and the head of the humerus is the *intertuberal bursa*, a sac filled with synovial fluid which protects and facilitates the movement of the biceps tendon in the *intertuberal groove*. Damage to this bursa is a common cause of shoulder lameness.

From the hindmost (or lower) edge of the scapula the long head of the triceps muscle takes its origin. This muscle, which lies beneath the front edge of the saddle flap in a hunter, inserts onto the point of the elbow and is a powerful extensor of the elbow joint, as well as having a flexing effect on the shoulder joint. It is a prominent landmark of the horse's shoulder region (Chart Two), and it provides a comfortable support at the front of the rider's shinbone. The teres major muscle also takes its origin from the lower border of the scapula and inserts onto the upper end of the humerus, the muscle being an important shoulder flexor.

The scapula of the horse varies in different individuals with regard to its degree of obliquity, i.e. the degree of angulation between the scapula and the horizontal. It is preferable that this angle should be as small as possible, an upright scapula accompanying a 'straight shoulder' being undesirable. The degree of inclination of the scapula depends on several factors. One of these is the length of the scapula itself. A long scapula must necessarily be inclined back, while a short one can stand erect. The next proviso is the length of the thoracic spines, as in all cases the upper end of the scapula is attached to the same spinal bones. When these spines are long and the bones to which the scapula is attached lie farther back, the scapula must be set more obliquely. A long scapula, well inclined, would seem to enable the horse to advance the humerus much farther than when this bone is set in a more upright position. If the humerus can be carried farther forward it follows that the knee and foot will follow suit. This makes for free front action and a long sweeping stride such as is required from a hack or hunter. Not only does an upright scapula spoil the shape of the withers and the set-on of the neck, but it also shortens the forward stride by moving through a considerably narrower angle.

THE SHOULDER JOINT

The shoulder joint is formed between the glenoid cavity of the scapula, its articular cup, and the articular head of the humerus. It is enclosed in a joint capsule which resembles a double-mouthed sac, one edge of which encircles the rim of the glenoid, while the other encircles the periphery of the humeral head. In spite of the great extent and considerable surface *it is the only joint in the limbs which has no definite collateral ligaments*. The two functions of these ligaments, maintaining articular continuity and directing the joint movements along habitual pathways, are subserved by numerous powerful muscles surrounding the joint. These help to hold the bones in apposition and include such muscles as the *supraspinatus*, *infraspinatus* and *subscapularis* which have already been noticed.

THE HUMERUS

Although the humerus is one of the strongest bones in the body it is not uncommonly shattered into numerous pieces during a seemingly straight gallop on the flat, not from any traumatic injury but purely as the outcome of imperfectly-timed muscular synchronization. It lies obliquely in the limb between the glenoid cavity of the scapula and the heads of the radius and ulna below (Fig. 13). Its upper end is large with a slightly convex *articular head* which is almost circular in shape in order to fit the glenoid cavity of the scapula. In front of the articular head is the well-marked *intertuberal* or *bicipital groove* between the *medial* and *lateral tuberosities*. The groove is divided by a central ridge into two channels and covered by a thick fibrocartilage. The tendon of the biceps muscle plays over it and the fibrocartilage is modelled to correspond with the face of the tendon to enable it to glide through the groove.

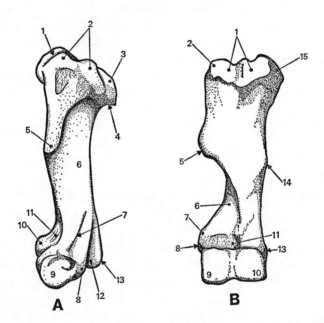

FIG. 13. Humerus of the left side in lateral view (A). Humerus of the right side in anterior view (B).
(1) Intertuberal groove. (2) Lateral tuberosity. (3) Head. (4) Neck. (5) Deltoid tuberosity. (6) Musculospiral groove. (7) Lateral condyloid crest. (8) Lateral epicondyle. (9) Lateral condyle. (10) Medial condyle. (11) Coronoid fossa. (12) Olecranon fossa. (13) Medial epicondyle. (14) Teres tuberosity. (15) Medial tuberosity.

A large pad of fat separates the biceps tendon from the shoulder joint capsule, and a *synovial bursa*, a sac filled with synovial fluid, facilitates the passage of the tendon through the groove. This bursa occupying as it does a most prominent position in the forelimb is quite likely to make forcible contact with articles not encountered when horses were first designed. Such things as the uprights holding up stable doors, the rails on racecourses and the posts holding jumps in place. Direct injury to the bursa may be the cause of serious and persistent lameness and in fact is probably the most frequent seat of shoulder lameness. Contrary to general belief however, shoulder lameness is by no means common in the horse.

The lateral tuberosity at the upper end of the humerus is large and divided into two parts. The anterior part borders the bicipital groove and gives attachment to the lateral branch of the supraspinatus tendon, the posterior part gives attachment to the infraspinatus muscle (Fig. 36). The medial tuberosity is smaller and also in two parts. The front part borders the inner side of the intertuberal groove and gives attachment to the medial branch of the supraspinatus tendon and the posterior deep pectoral muscle, the hind part gives attachment to the subscapular muscle.

The *shaft of the humerus* possesses a *musculospiral groove* winding around onto the front of the bone above the elbow. This lodges the brachialis muscle a flexor of the elbow joint. On the outer surface of the shaft, a little less than halfway down, the *deltoid tuberosity* juts out to give attachment to the deltoid muscle. This prominence can easily be palpated through the horse's skin (Chart Two) and as it is so prominent it sometimes becomes injured in collisions and may give rise to lameness. On the medial surface of the shaft, a smaller prominence, the *teres tuberosity*, provides attachment for the teres major and latissimus dorsi muscles, two of the main limb retractor muscles. The humeral shaft also provides areas on its posterior surface for the origin of the shorter heads of the triceps muscle (the lateral and medial heads).

At its lower end the humerus has an oblique *trochlear surface* (a deep groove between two prominent smooth condyles) for articulation with the radius and ulna. Each condyle also supports on its lateral surface an *epicondyle* for origin of some of the flexor

and extensor muscles to the forearm. The *medial epicondyle* is by
far the larger of the two and projects posteriorly behind the level
of the articular surface of the elbow joint. It is an important
structure since it gives origin to parts of the deep digital flexor
and superficial digital flexor muscles which play an important
role in elbow fixation since they both have tendinous components
extending throughout their bellies. Other parts of these digital
flexor muscles originate lower down on the olecranon process
and the surface of the radius and ulna. On the hind surface of
the humerus at its lower end a large excavation, the *olecranon
fossa* lies between the epicondyles. This fossa receives the *anconeal
process* of the ulna when the elbow joint is extended.

THE RADIUS AND ULNA

The *radius* of the horse is larger than the *ulna* to which it is united
by ligamentous fibres in the young animal, and rigidly by solid
bone in the adult (Fig. 14). In the normal standing position the
radius is held approximately vertical and the angle between the
obliquely inclined humerus and the radius at the elbow is 145
degrees. There is no movement between radius and ulna in the
horse. In ourselves the bones move freely on one another enabling
us to turn the palm of the hand upwards (supinate) or downwards
(pronate).

The upper end of the radius forms an articular surface in conjunction with the ulna, which is moulded upon that of the lower
articular surface of the humerus. The *radial articular surface* is
bounded by a well defined rim and the middle of its articular
portion carries a raised projection, the *coronoid process*. The lateral
surface of the upper end of the radius is an important area since
parts of the common digital and lateral digital extensor muscles
arise from it. Carpal and digital flexor components arise from the
olecranon process of the ulna and the posterior surfaces of both
radius and ulna. However, we have already seen that the bulk
of the digital flexor muscles come from the medial epicondyle
of the humerus, as does the bulk of the carpal flexor mass
(flexor carpi radialis, flexor carpi ulnaris). However, one
carpal flexor, the ulnaris lateralis, does have an origin on the
lateral epicondyle of the humerus.

The lower end of the radius is provided with a *carpal articular*

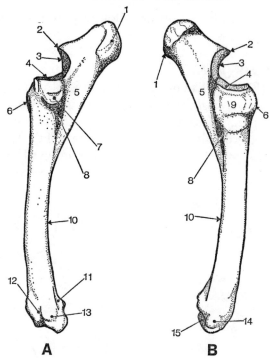

FIG. 14. Radius and ulna of the left side.
A. Lateral view. B. Medial view.

(1) Olecranon process. (2) Anconeal process. (3) Semilunar notch. (4) Humeral articular surface. (5) Shaft of the ulna. (6) Radial tuberosity. (7) Lateral tuberosity for the attachment of extensor muscles. (8) Interosseous space. (9) Medial tuberosity. (10) Shaft of radius. (11) Groove for lateral extensor tendon. (12) Groove for common extensor tendon. (13) Tuberosity for the lateral carpal ligament. (14) Tuberosity for the medial carpal ligament. (15) Carpal articular surface.

surface carrying several facets which correspond with those of the upper row of carpal or knee bones.

Whereas in man, and most other animals, the ulna is larger than the radius, in the horse it is small and short apart from its hindmost large projection, the *olecranon process*. This is a massive structure projecting upward and somewhat backward behind the lower end of the humerus forming a lever arm for the extensor muscles (triceps) of the elbow. It has an outer convex surface and an anterior edge terminating in a beak-like structure, the *anconeal process*, which is housed in the olecranon fossa between the epicondyles on the lower end of the humerus. The ulna is noteworthy in having no central marrow cavity which other long bones of the limbs possess. The body of the ulna is a triangular portion of bone with its apex at its lowest part a little above the centre of the radius.

THE ELBOW JOINT

The elbow (Fig. 15), like most of the limb joints, is an example of what is termed a *ginglymus*, a hinge-like joint which moves only in one direction, without lateral movements. However, it does differ in that the position of maximum contact of the two articular surfaces is the middle position, i.e. not the flexed or extended

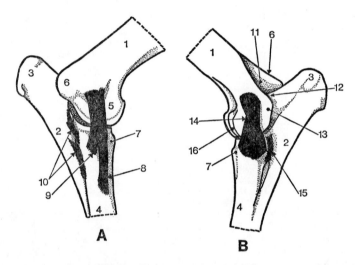

FIG. 15. Elbow joint of the left side.
A. Medial view. B. Lateral view.
(1) Humerus. (2) Shaft of the ulna. (3) Olecranon process. (4) Radius. (5) Medial condyle. (6) Medial epicondyle. (7) Radial tuberosity. (8) Long medial collateral ligament. (9) Short medial collateral ligament. (10) Medial transverse radioulnar ligament. (11) Olecranon fossa. (12) Anconeal process. (13) Lateral epicondyle. (14) Lateral collateral ligament. (15) Lateral transverse radioulnar ligament. (16) Humeral trochlea.

positions as in most other limb joints. The middle position, or the position of maximum joint stability of the elbow, lies between 140 and 150 degrees dorsal angle which is the normal standing angle. The elbow joint is 'braced' in this position by its *collateral ligaments*, by muscular cooperation between the elbow flexors and extensors and by muscular action of the digital flexors originating on the medial epicondyle. During elbow flexion the collateral ligaments loosen and the bones of the forearm (radius and ulna) do not move in the exact plane of the humerus, but rotate a little outwards around the anatomical axis of the radius. When this peculiarity is overpronounced the horse throws its forefoot a little outwards during elbow flexion especially when trotting. It is then said to 'dish'.

Owing to the passage of the anconeal process into the olecranon fossa of the humerus, aided by the strong collateral ligaments which hold radius and ulna together, and the biceps muscle and cranial ligament of the joint, overextension of the elbow is prevented. The bones of the arm and forearm cannot therefore be brought into the same straight line.

THE CARPUS OR KNEE

There are usually seven carpal bones, but there may sometimes be eight, arranged in two rows one above the other. The bones of the upper row are: *radial carpal* (scaphoid), *intermediate carpal* (semilunar), *ulnar carpal* (cuneiform) and the *accessory carpal* (pisiform) at the back. Those of the lower row are: *first carpal* (trapezium), *second carpal* (trapezoid), *third carpal* (os magnum) and *fourth carpal* (unciform). The disposition and relationships of the carpal bones will be better understood by reference to Figs. 16 and 17.

The *accessory carpal* is a flattened, four-sided bone which articulates with the rear of the ulnar carpal on the outer side of the back of the carpus, and the radius above. The inner surface is concave and forms, with the posterior surface of the radial and intermediate carpals, the *carpal groove*. This is converted into a *carpal canal* by deep and superficial ligaments, through which the tendons of the deep and superficial flexor muscles pass down behind the knee within the *carpal synovial sheath*. The outer surface of the accessory carpal bone carries a furrow (Fig. 17A), down which the long tendon of the ulnaris lateralis muscle passes. The accessory carpal does not bear weight directly, being a sesamoid bone which is interposed in the course of the tendons of the middle and lateral carpal flexors (flexor carpi ulnaris and ulnaris lateralis). It enables these muscles to work at a mechanical advantage giving greater leverage since the bone takes on the role of a pulley-block.

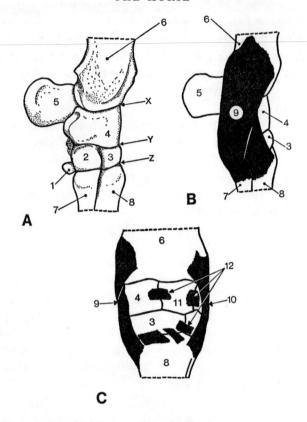

FIG. 16. Carpus of the left side.
A. Medial view. B. Medial view showing the main ligaments. C. Anterior view showing the main ligaments.
(1) First carpal. (2) Second carpal. (3) Third carpal. (4) Radial carpal. (5) Accessory carpal. (6) Radius. (7) Small metacarpal bone. (8) Large metacarpal bone. (9) Medial collateral ligament. (10) Lateral collateral ligament. (11) Intermediate carpal. (12) Short dorsal carpal ligaments. (X) Radiocarpal joint. (Y) Intercarpal joint. (Z) Carpometacarpal joint.

MOVEMENTS OF THE KNEE JOINT

The carpus or knee joint can be considered as another ginglymus in that it moves only in one direction, that of extension and flexion, without lateral or rotatory movements. However, when the knee is flexed with the foot carried behind it, with its innermost bar making contact with the point of the elbow, the joint can be seen to be a compound one containing three subsidiary joints. A gap forms at the front of the knee between the radius and the upper

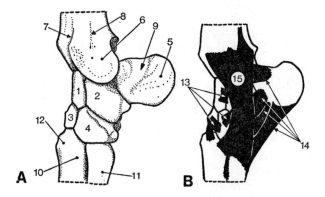

FIG. 17. Carpus of the left side.
A. Lateral view. B. Lateral view showing the main ligaments.
(1) Intermediate carpal. (2) Ulnar carpal. (3) Third carpal. (4) Fourth carpal.
(5) Accessory carpal. (6) Radius. (7) Groove for common extensor tendon. (8)
Groove for lateral extensor tendon. (9) Groove for ulnaris lateralis tendon. (10) Large
metacarpal bone. (11) Small metacarpal bone. (12) Metacarpal tuberosity.
(13) Short dorsal ligaments. (14) Ligaments of accessory carpal. (15) Lateral
collateral ligament.

row of carpal bones (*radio-carpal joint*), and a second gap between
the two rows of carpal bones (*intercarpal joint*). A third gap is
hardly noticeable, that between the lower rows of carpal bones
and the metacarpus (*carpo-metacarpal joint*). This movement is
provided for by the manner in which the carpal bone connecting
ligaments are arranged (Fig. 16C), and by the slackness of the
anterior carpal ligament, which in the extended state of the carpus is
quite loose in fit.

During extension of the carpal joint, movement is arrested when
the large metacarpal bone comes into line with the radius of the
forearm. Mainly owing to the fact that the back of the knee is
contained within a thick, strong, *posterior* or *volar carpal ligament*
(the deep lining of the carpal canal), and by other ligaments
between the radius and carpus, and also between the rows of
bones. The volar carpal ligament is continued down as the
subcarpal or *inferior check ligament* to blend with the deep flexor
tendon (Fig. 40). This structure has some significance in the stay
apparatus to be elucidated later in Part Three.

The carpal joints are set slightly obliquely so that during knee
flexion the foot turns outwards a little from the central plane
of the forearm. When the knee is fully flexed the strong *collateral*

ligaments relax sufficiently to permit slight movements of the foot outwardly and inwardly (abduction and adduction). This can be verified by lifting the foot and flexing the knee (bending it backward), and observing the position of the now upturned sole which does not meet the point of the elbow excepting at its innermost heel. In cases of 'capped elbow' it is usually the inner heel of the shoe which causes bruising by making contact with the point of the elbow while the horse is lying.

The tendons of the extensor muscles of the digit pass over the front of the knee enclosed in *synovial sheaths* to ensure smooth passage. We have already seen a synovial bursa beneath the biceps tendon. A synovial sheath differs from a bursa in that the synovial sac is wrapped around the tendon. The inner layer of the sheath is attached to the tendon, the outer layer, in this case, lines the carpal canal in which the tendon runs. The two layers can glide over one another freely being lubricated by the synovial fluid between them. These tendons can be felt with the fingers, and if their synovial sheaths become distended their positions can easily be seen.

THE METACARPAL BONES

Three *metacarpal bones* are present two of which, together with their attendant digits, have regressed until they serve no practical purpose other than as support for some of the carpal bones. As marsh-dwellers the ancestors of the modern horse benefited from having three functional toes. Today, on firm ground, the horse manages quite well with a single toe on each foot. The two toes which have undergone reduction are only represented by the *small metacarpal bones* or *splint bones*. These reduced digits are equivalent to the index and ring fingers of your hand, while the large metacarpal or cannon bone, is the equivalent of your middle finger.

The shaft of the *large metacarpal bone* (Fig. 18) is slender but capable of carrying a great deal of weight. Its strength depends upon the thickness of the solid bone surrounding the cancellous or spongy medullary cavity which is small in extent, the metacarpal being almost completely solid bone throughout. The term 'bone' as applied by horsemen and judges to the metacarpal region of the horse is something of a misnomer. No-one can judge

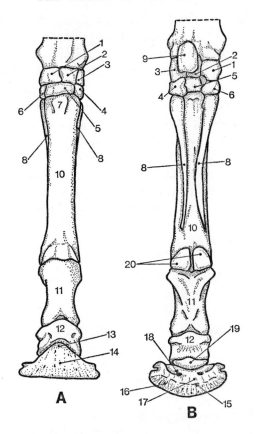

FIG. 18. Left limb below the knee.
A. Anterior view. B. Posterior view. (After Taylor)
(1) Radial carpal. (2) Intermediate carpal. (3) Ulnar carpal. (4) Fourth carpal. (5) Third carpal. (6) Second carpal. (7) Metacarpal tuberosity. (8) Small metacarpals. (9) Accessory carpal. (10) Large metacarpal. (11) First phalanx. (12) Second phalanx. (13) Extensor process. (14) Third phalanx. (15) Semilunar crest. (16) Solar area. (17) Flexor area. (18) Arterial foramen. (19) Distal sesamoid bone. (20) Proximal sesamoid bones.

the thickness, strength or quality of a metacarpal bone with anything less than an X-ray examination during life, and by the examination of sections and determination of its chemical composition after death. It is unlikely that the judge who grips the cannon between the thumb and fingers and decides on its thickness, flatness or roundness, by touch alone, would be able to recognize the particular metacarpal bone or distinguish it from that of any one of a dozen other competitors if it were removed from the limb, boiled out and presented to him on a plate. One bone, whatever its shape on section, whether round, flat or triangular, differs from another only in the density of the bone underlying its periosteum and its chemical composition. Beneath the periosteum lies a circle of hard bone, harder near the surface and gradually softening as it reaches the centre. Some bones contain more or less compact bone than others, but externally all look much the same. The fact is that what is handled and described as 'bone' includes the metacarpal bones, the periosteum, a number of tendons, blood-vessels and nerves, the suspensory and check ligaments, a variable amount of connective tissue between and surrounding the tendons, and the overlying skin.

About three-quarters of the upper articular surface of the head of the large metacarpal bone supports the third carpal. On its outer side the fourth carpal bone articulates, and on its inner side the second carpal. At the front of the head, immediately below the knee, is a prominence, the *metacarpal tuberosity*, onto which the tendon of the extensor carpi radialis muscle inserts, and along with it the lacertus fibrosus from the biceps muscle which has blended with the carpal extensor tendon. This is an important element of the stay apparatus (Fig. 40). At the back of the meta-carpal head, and on either side, is a facet which forms a synovial joint with the appropriate small metacarpal bone. The lower end of the large metacarpal bone has basically two articulatory areas. One articulates below with the first phalanx, and the second with the proximal sesamoid bones at its rear.

The *splint bones* represent aborted long bones lacking any medullary cavity. The inner is usually larger than the outer, but each is three-sided and slightly curved with the concavity directed outwards. The upper ends of these bones aid in the support of the lower row of carpal bones. The inner splint articulates with the second and third carpal bones, the outer splint with the fourth carpal bone. The lower end of each terminates in a small rounded button.

The hind surface of the large metacarpal bone is flattened from side to side, and with the small metacarpals, forms a wide groove which houses the *suspensory ligament*. Up to 3 or 4 years the union between large and small metacarpal bones is fibrous and some up and down movement is transferred to the splint bones from knee movements during locomotion. The movement, especially near the union between the bones, may set up an inflammatory reaction in the periosteal covering of both large and small metacarpals, and give rise to the condition referred to as 'splints'. This is a frequent cause of lameness in young horses. However, it is a condition which usually recovers when the bones become firmly fused either from age or from post-inflammatory union brought about by the deposition of fresh bone between the large and smaller bones. Such inflammatory changes may be ascribed to: (a) heredity; (b) conformation; (c) concussion resulting from excessive exercise on hard roads; (d) blows or other injury; (e) the pull exerted on the bone and its covering by the extensor and flexor muscles of the carpus (the oblique extensor muscle and the flexor carpi radialis muscles have tendons inserted on the head of the inner small metacarpal bone).

Inflammation of the periosteum covering the metacarpal bones may give rise to the condition, common in racehorses, known as 'sore shins'. This results from concussion but may also be influenced by the pull of tendons, notably that of the extensor carpi radialis muscle whose tendon inserts onto the head of the large metacarpal bone.

THE PHALANGES
(1) First phalanx
This is a long bone occupying an oblique position between the lower end of the large metacarpal bone and the upper end of the second phalanx (Fig. 18). Its upper extremity is deeply grooved and divided into two articular surfaces moulded upon that at the lower end of the metacarpal bone. The inner section, as is usually the case, is the larger and wider, and it is on account of this slight disparity that the foot travels forward in a straight line with the mid-plane of the body and without unnecessary deviation in either lateral direction. But slight abnormalities or deviations in the relative sizes of the divided segments of articular surface may be hereditary and accordingly certain defects of action, perhaps not amounting to unsoundness, may be transmitted to progeny. This gives rise to some impairment to the gait with faulty handling of the lower portions of the forelimb.

The lower end of the first phalanx is also divided into two

articular surfaces with the inner the larger, but the line of division is not so distinct as at the upper end of the bone. At the front of the upper end there is a prominence for the attachment of the common digital extensor tendon, while at the back of the lower end on either side the superficial digital flexor tendon attaches.

(2) *Second phalanx*

This is a short bone without a medullary cavity and is therefore solid throughout. It is of great importance because it is half inside and half above the upper limit of the wall of the hoof

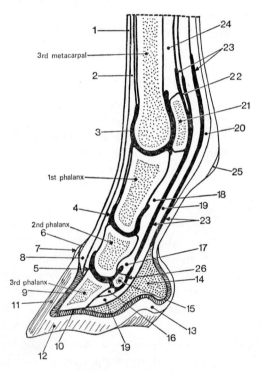

FIG. 19. Diagrammatic vertical section of the limb below the knee.
(1) Skin. (2) Common digital extensor tendon. (3) Capsule of fetlock joint. (4) Capsule of pastern joint. (5) Capsule of coffin joint. (6) Corium of periople. (7) Periople. (8) Coronary corium. (9) Laminar corium. (10) Corium of sole. (11) Wall. (12) Sole. (13) Frog. (14) Digital cushion. (15) Navicular bone. (16) Distal ligament of navicular. (17) Suspensory ligament of navicular. (18) Inferior sesamoidean ligament. (19) Deep digital flexor tendon. (20) Superficial digital flexor tendon. (21) Proximal sesamoid bone. (22) Ring formed from superficial flexor tendon. (23) Digital synovial sheath. (24) Suspensory ligament. (25) Ergot. (26) Navicular bursa.

(Fig. 19), and it is also the first free limb bone to sustain concussion
as the foot hits the ground. This is probably why it is so often
involved in the condition known as 'ringbone', especially as it
projects above the hoof to support the coronet. It is easily palpable at this point as it projects above the hoof and is susceptible to
external injury. It must not be concluded from this that any great
percentage of bony enlargements of the coronet arise from this
cause. Many cases of 'low ringbone' commence at the extensor
process (pyramidal process) on the front of the upper end of the
third phalanx, and extend to the second phalanx later. Such cases
may arise from the effects of concussion upon a bone in which
hereditary influences are already involved.

The second phalanx lies somewhat obliquely and is supported
along its posterior surface by the deep flexor tendon which runs
along a groove in the bone which is covered by a plate of fibrocartilage (Figs. 21 and 47). The common extensor tendon has an
attachment to the front surface of the bone, the superficial flexor
tendon attaches to its volar surface just like the first phalanx.
The fact that this bone is not upright and that it is, in a sense,
cradled by the deep flexor tendon probably does a great deal to
lessen the degree of concussion it might otherwise be compelled
to withstand.

(3) *Third phalanx*

This terminal bone of the limb much resembles the hoof in shape
(Fig. 20), but is very much smaller and occupies only a minor
portion of the cavity within the hoof. The wall surface slopes

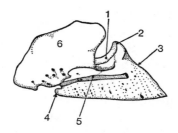

FIG. 20. Third phalanx in lateral view.
(1) Articular surface of coffin joint. (2) Extensor process. (3) Dorsal surface.
(4) Angle. (5) Dorsal groove. (6) Lateral cartilage.

downward and forward and is roughened and pitted by numerous holes. The volar or under surface is divided by a curved line, the *semilunar crest*, into a crescent-shaped *sole surface* in front, and a *flexor surface* behind. The deep digital flexor tendon is attached by a fan-like tendon to the edges of the semilunar crest and the flexor surface (Fig. 47). A space is left between the deep flexor tendon and the upper part of the hind face of the bone which is occupied by the *distal sesamoid* (navicular) bone (Fig. 18). Beneath the third phalanx and the deep flexor tendon there is a space filled by a fibroelastic pad known as the *digital cushion* (Fig. 19). This pad is moulded over the inner face of the horny frog into which it is partly embedded by papillae which project from it and enter pores in the horn structure. The purpose of the digital cushion is to act as a buffer and lessen concussion when the foot meets the ground.

The third phalanx is well supported within the horny wall of the hoof owing to the production of *sensitive laminae* from the *corium* covering the bone which interleave with *horny, insensitive laminae* lining the wall. The surface of the third phalanx is punctured in a great many places by small holes through which blood vessels pass into and out of the bone. The vascular system within the hoof is rather complicated but basically consists of two terminal, *digital arteries*, which enter the third phalanx one on either side of its undersurface (Fig. 18). These arteries meet and coalesce in the centre of the bone. The *terminal arch* so produced gives off a large number of radiating branches which pass through bony canals and emerge dorsally to supply all the tissues inside the hoof. Blood flow is directed away from the foot through a complex interwoven network of veins, the *coronary plexus*, encircling the third phalanx, covering the terminal part of the extensor tendon and the lateral cartilages of the third phalanx.

The highest point of the third phalanx is the *extensor process* at the front of the articular surface. This gives attachment to the tendon of the common digital extensor which advances the foot and extends the fetlock and knee joints. The articular surface of the third phalanx is moulded to that of the lower end of the second phalanx. It also carries a flattened facet at its most posterior portion which articulates with the distal sesamoid bone.

The *angles* of the third phalanx on either side are divided into two backwardly directed processes by a deep notch which in aged horses becomes converted by a deposit of bone into a foramen. The two angles give support to the *lateral cartilages* of the foot (Fig. 20). These cartilages are composed of hyaline cartilage in the young subject but later become fibrous. Their outer surface is convex and their inner concave. On this inner aspect they join up with the digital cushion and in front afford protection to the articulation between the second and third phalanges. The upper border of each cartilage is thin and flexible. It can be moved sideways with the finger and it bulges outwards everytime weight falls on the heel and frog. In old horses these cartilages often become infiltrated with bone to give rise to a situation in which the angles of the third phalanx are larger than normal and undivided except for the passage of a foramen. The lateral cartilages can easily be felt at the hinder and lateral edges of the *coronet* above the cavity of the heel. When the foot is lifted off the ground each cartilage can be squeezed between fingers and thumb. It is then easy to determine whether the cartilages are free and supple or if they are becoming calcified. This process of calcification commences at the front end and in a young horse it is referred to as 'sidebone'. Lameness is said to result from it, but it is nevertheless true that the majority of horses exhibiting calcified lateral cartilages go sound unless there is some other lesion present such as ringbone.

With these factors concerning the third phalanx in mind we can see how the foot succeeds in maintaining an efficient circulation. The blood reaches the foot very easily, especially as all the arteries are pumping blood 'downhill', but forcing the blood up the limb away from the foot is not so easy. It is helped a great deal by the pumping action set up by the *frog* which is compressed when the foot lands on the ground. This causes the elastic digital cushion to be thrust upwards between the two cartilages exerting pressures sufficient to squeeze blood out of the vessels and back up the veins to the body. It must be stressed that this can only be effected when the frog actually makes contact with the ground. If the frog has been trimmed well back and the heel of the shoe is thick, the pumping action, which is an integral part of the machinery of the equine foot, may cease. Congestion of the foot results which may end up in laminitis.

THE SESAMOID BONES

(1) Proximal sesamoids

These two small bones lie one on either side at the back of the lower end of the large metacarpal bone with which they articulate. Each sesamoid is a three-sided pyramid. The anterior face is concave and moulded to correspond with the hinder end of the metacarpal bone at its lower end. The posterior surfaces of the two bones as they lie side by side provide a smooth channel which is further covered by fibrocartilage, the *intersesamoidean ligament*. At this level the superficial digital flexor tendon is in the form of a ring through which the deep digital flexor tendon glides (Fig. 19). These tendons are bound down in the sesamoid groove by the *volar annular ligament* of the fetlock.

The sesamoids act jointly as a pulley block over which the deep flexor tendon runs. The tendons are moved further away from the centre of rotation (the joint axis) imparting a considerable increase in leverage. This increase in the mechanical advantage is utilised in resisting rotation of the *metacarpo-phalangeal joint (fetlock)*. The sesamoids are also intercalated in the suspensory apparatus with very strong ligaments above, below, laterally and transversely. This suspensory apparatus serves to increase the surface area of the fetlock joint and to receive the compression force transmitted through the large metacarpal bone. It can be well understood that under the conditions imposed upon horses in modern times these two sesamoid bones are subjected to a very great degree of strain and to almost overwhelming pressure on occasion.

(2) Distal sesamoid

The *distal sesamoid* or *navicular bone* is small and shuttle-shaped, lying behind the articulation between second and third phalanges. Its articular surface is directed upwards and forwards to articulate with the hinder part of the lower articular surface of the second phalanx. Its lower edge has another, articular portion anteriorly in the form of a transversely elongated, flat facet which articulates with a similar surface at the back of the third phalanx between its two heel-like projections.

The tendon surface of the navicular bone is directed downwards and backwards. It is covered by fibrocartilage to make a smooth bed over which the deep digital flexor tendon travels before it spreads out in fan-like fashion to insert into the semilunar crest on the undersurface of the third phalanx (Figs. 19 and 47).

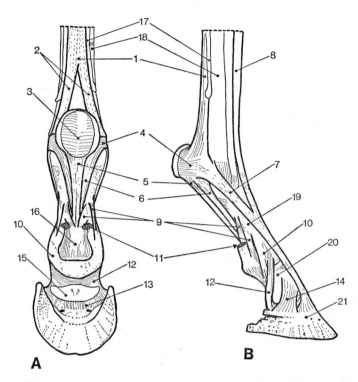

FIG. 21. Left limb below the knee showing the suspensory apparatus.
A. Posterior view. B. Lateral view. (After Bradley.)
(1) Suspensory ligament. (2) Bifurcation of ligament. (3) Intersesamoidean ligament. (4) Collateral sesamoidean ligament. (5) Straight distal sesamoidean ligament. (6) Oblique distal sesamoidean ligament. (7) Suspensory ligament branch to common extensor tendon. (8) Common digital extensor tendon. (9) Volar ligaments of pastern joint. (10) Lateral ligaments of pastern joint. (11) Cut stump of superficial digital flexor tendon. (12) Suspensory ligament of navicular. (13) Distal navicular ligament. (14) Collateral ligament of coffin joint. (15) Navicular bone. (16) Fibrous plate. (17) Small metacarpal. (18) Large metacarpal. (19) First phalanx. (20) Second phalanx. (21) Third phalanx.

THE SUSPENSORY APPARATUS

A number of important ligaments are connected with the sesamoid bones to form a brace or suspensory apparatus, an integral part of the overall *stay apparatus* to be outlined in Part Three. The sesamoid bones are actually intercalated within the ligaments.

The disposition of the suspensory apparatus will be better understood by reference to Fig 21.

The *suspensory* or *superior sesamoidean ligament* lies in the metacarpal groove originating from the back of the lower row of carpal bones and the adjacent part of the large metacarpal bone. It divides into two branches lower down, one passing into each of the proximal sesamoid bones. The ligaments then pass forwards to the front surface of the first phalanx to join the tendon of the common digital extensor.

The *intersesamoidean ligament* has already been noticed as the mass of fibrocartilage in which the proximal sesamoid bones are largely embedded, the underside forming a smooth groove for the tendon of the deep digital flexor muscle.

The *collateral sesamoidean ligaments* lie on either side of the fetlock joint extending from the proximal sesamoid bones to the lower end of the large metacarpal bone and to the upper end of the first phalanx.

The *inferior sesamoidean ligaments* are a series of separate ligaments running down from the sesamoid bones onto the first phalanx (and also in one case the second phalanx). These are all digital continuations of the suspensory ligament.

The suspensory ligament, being a modified muscle, still contains some muscle tissue and possesses considerable elasticity, its principal function being to support the fetlock joint preventing excessive dorsiflexion (overextension). As we shall see later on, the supporting function is aided by the tendons of both superficial and deep flexor muscles. The suspensory ligament together with the proximal sesamoid bones carry most of the weight of the horse at many stages of locomotion.

The *fetlock joint* is a typical ginglymus, exhibiting only flexion and extension movements. It is however, subjected to the greatest stress of any limb joint, and at times the entire body weight may be pressed down on a single fetlock joint. In the normal standing position the joint capsule is voluminous behind and allows a great deal of movement. Overextension (excessive dorsiflexion) is limited by the sesamoidean apparatus, together with the fetlock joints own *collateral ligaments*. Volar flexion is limited only by the contact of the heel with the metacarpus.

The *pastern joint* (*proximal interphalangeal joint*) lies between the first and second phalanges and is the least movable of the phalangeal joints. In the normal standing position the joint is extended. A small amount of volar flexion is possible but is limited by the tendon of the common digital extensor in front, and possibly at some stages of movement by the suspensory ligament extensions from the sesamoids onto the common extensor tendon. Excessive dorsiflexion is prevented by the *collateral ligaments* of the joint and by *volar ligaments* on the underside between the first and second phalanges. These volar ligaments thus have considerable importance in bearing weight at the back of the digit. The *straight ligament* (one of the inferior sesamoidean group of ligaments) attaches onto the second phalanx and helps to support the pastern joint.

The *coffin joint* (*distal interphalangeal joint*) lies within the hoof between the second and third phalanges. It exhibits a great degree of movement and so has a structure which approaches that of the fetlock rather than the pastern joint. On the underside the navicular bone takes part in the formation of the joint, and has a series of specific ligaments associated with it. These are somewhat elastic and form a suspensory apparatus involved in digital support. These *suspensory navicular ligaments* are attached at their upper ends to the lower part of the second phalanx blending with the pastern ligaments as they pass down to attach to the navicular bone. This bone is supported below by the *distal navicular ligament* passing onto the semilunar crest area of the third phalanx. In the normal standing position the joint is extended, over-extension being limited by the suspensory navicular apparatus and the tendon of the deep digital flexor muscle.

THE HINDLIMB

The hindlimb differs from the forelimb in the fact that it is directly attached, through a bony union, with the spine. This means that propulsive forces generated by the hindlimbs will be transmitted directly onto the vertebral column, but it also means that concussive forces are transmitted up the limb to the spine.

From above to below the bones of the hindlimb are: (a) the *os coxae* or *pelvic bone*; (b) the *femur* or *thigh bone* which reaches from the hip joint to the stifle joint (the large sesamoid bone, the *patella*, lies at the front of the lower end of the femur); (c) the *tibia* and *fibula*, extending from the stifle joint to the hock joint (the fibula is greatly reduced in extent); (d) the *tarsus* or *hock*, made up of six bones; (e) the *metatarsal bones* and *phalanges*, which differ in no significant respects from the metacarpals and phalanges of the forelimb.

THE PELVIC GIRDLE

The *pelvic girdle* consists of two equal halves (*pelvic bones*) welded together in adult life (Fig. 22). These bones, together with the sacrum and the first three coccygeal vertebrae, form the bony walls of the pelvis surrounding the pelvic cavity. This cavity houses the rectum and bladder (when empty), the posterior part of the uterus, vagina and vulva in the mare, and some parts of the genital tract of the stallion. In the mare it also provides the passage through which the foetus must pass during the process of birth.

Each half of the girdle is made up of three flat bones fused together into one composite bone. The upper portion of the pelvic bone, that part which attaches to the sacrum, is formed from the *ilium*; the front portion of the pelvic floor lying between the hind-limbs is the *pubis*; the hindmost portion of the pelvic floor consists of the *ischium*. These three bones all meet at one point and in so doing they give rise to the large, cup-shaped, articular cavity known as the *acetabulum*, which houses the head of the femur to form the hip joint.

The *ilium* is the largest portion. It is flattened above into a roughly triangular plate which forms part of the roof and outer wall of the pelvic cavity. Its outermost angle is enlarged as the *tuber coxae* and gives shape to the *haunch* or pin, the most prominent part of the hindquarters on either side. The inner angle of the triangular, upper part of the ilium, the *tuber sacrale*, approximates its fellow where they join the sacrum, being firmly united to it by the short, strong *sacroiliac ligament*. The eminence formed by these bones at the highest point of the hindquarters produces the slight eminence known as the *croup*.

The *pubis* and *ischium* combine to form the pelvic floor and meet their opposite numbers at the *pelvic symphysis* mid-ventrally. In the foal the bones are joined by a layer of fibrocartilage. In the adult this is largely replaced by bone and no appreciable move-

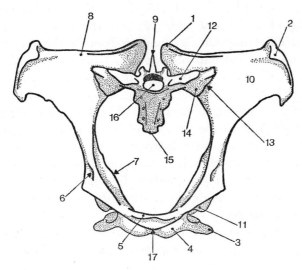

FIG. 22. Pelvis in anteroventral view showing the relationship of the pelvic bones and
sacrum.
(1) Tuber sacrale. (2) Tuber coxae. (3) Tuber ischii. (4) Ischium. (5) Pubis.
(6) Point of origin of the rectus femoris muscle. (7) Ischiatic spine. (8) Crest of
ilium. (9) Sacral spinous process. (10) Pelvic surface of ilium. (11) Acetabulum.
(12) Articulatory surface for the transverse process of the last lumbar vertebra.
(13) Sacroiliac joint. (14) Wing of sacrum. (15) Apex of sacrum. (16) Body of
sacral vertebra. (17) Pelvic symphysis.

ment occurs even in the mare. The *obturator foramen* is a large
perforation on either side of the pelvic symphysis between the
pubis and ischium, which is covered over by a membranous sheet
for the most part but does give passage to nerves and blood
vessels. The ischium is thickened at the back as the *tuber ischii* or
seat bone.

The *pelvic cavity* is the last of the three major body cavities,
the others being the thorax and abdomen. It is tubular in shape
and continuous with the abdominal cavity, though the pubic
bones cross the front end of the floor transversely and are apt to
cause some partial obstruction especially in deep-bellied mares.

The boundaries of the pelvic cavity become apparent when an
examination is made with the hand and arm inserted into the
rectum up to the elbow. The roof is formed by the sacrum, the
first three coccygeal vertebrae and the flattened, triangular portions of the ilium. The walls are supported by the two shafts of

the ilia, one on either side, and also by a tense membranous sheet consisting of the *lateral sacroiliac* and the *sacrosciatic ligaments* (Fig. 23). This composite ligamentous sheet fills the space between the sacrum and first pair of coccygeal bones and the ilium and ischium. The lower border of the ligament leaves two gaps between it and the border of the pelvic bone, the *greater* and *lesser sciatic foramina* for the passage of nerves and blood vessels to the muscles of the rump and to the muscles of much of the hindleg. The hindborder of the ligament is fused with part of the semimembranosus muscle which originates from the first two coccygeal vertebrae and from the sacrosciatic ligament itself. The floor of the pelvic cavity is made up of the pubic bones and ischia on either side of the pelvic symphysis.

The pelvic bones provide extensive areas for muscle attachment, many of the muscles being especially important in locomotion.

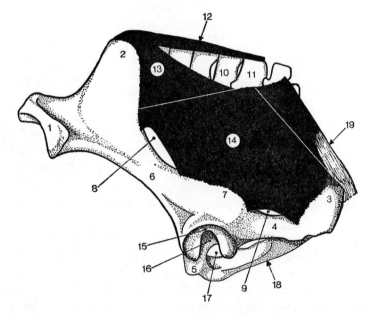

FIG. 23. Pelvis in lateral view showing the ligamentous wall of the pelvic cavity. (1) Tuber coxae. (2) Tuber sacrale. (3) Tuber ischii. (4) Ischium. (5) Pubis. (6) Shaft of ilium. (7) Superior ischiatic spine. (8) Greater sciatic foramen. (9) Lesser sciatic foramen. (10) Spinous process of sacral vertebra. (11) Spinous process of first coccygeal vertebra. (12) Dorsal sacroiliac ligament. (13) Lateral sacroiliac ligament. (14) Sacrosciatic ligament. (15) Acetabulum. (16) Acetabular notch. (17) Obturator foramen. (18) Pelvic symphysis. (19) Semimembranosus muscle.

The tuber coxae and the adjacent part of the ilium give origin to the tensor fasciae latae and the superficial gluteal muscles. The remainder of the iliac shaft and the outer face of the sacrosciatic ligament give origin to the middle and deep gluteal muscles. Behind the hip joint the sacrosciatic ligament, the first two coccygeal vertebrae, and the tuber ischii give origin to the hamstring muscles (biceps femoris, semitendinosus and semimembranosus). On the inner side of the hip joint the ventral parts of the ischium and pubis, in the region of the pelvic symphysis, give origin to the gracilis and adductor muscles.

The front opening of the pelvic cavity, the *pelvic inlet*, faces obliquely downwards and forwards. The size and shape of the pelvic cavity differs between the two sexes. The external diameter of the pelvis determines the width of the horse's hindquarters, while the internal diameter of the pelvic cavity varies, being wider and more circular in the mare, narrower and more upright in the stallion and gelding.

The cavity of the female pelvis is considerably larger than that of the male, the acetabula are farther apart and so are the seat bones, thus the *pelvic outlet* in the mare is larger. The obturator foramina are also larger in the mare and the pelvic floor is wider and flatter. The overall diameter of the inside of the pelvis is also influenced by the angle at which the sacrum lies in relation to the pelvic floor. When the sacrum is tilted downwards it may partially occlude the pelvic circle or at least make it shorter. This may cause difficulty in foaling. Difficulty may also arise when the sacrum is excessively long, but still horizontal, and especially when the distance between the seat bones and the haunches is excessive. These factors are not uncommonly encountered in mares carrying a good deal of Arab blood.

THE HIP JOINT

This joint (Fig. 24) is made up from the head of the femur and the acetabulum. The latter is a deep articular cup situated at the junction of the ilium, pubis and ischium. The rim of this *cotyloid cavity* is deeply cut into medially by the *acetabular notch*. The total depth of the cup is increased by the presence of an added fibrocartilaginous ring, the *cotyloid ligament* attached to the bony rim of the acetabulum. Part of the cotyloid ligament crosses the acetabular notch as the *transverse acetabular ligament*. The whole of the surface of the bowl is not covered with articular cartilage and a corresponding non-articular notch is present on the head of the femur. Into these two gaps two structures are attached. One is the short, *round* or *teres ligament* passing from the head of the femur into the articular gap in the acetabular bowl; the other is the *accessory ligament*, a structure only present in the Horse family. It originates from the opposite prepubic tendon of the abdominal muscles. It crosses its fellow tendon in front of the pubis and enters the acetabulum through the acetabular notch, held in place by the transverse acetabular ligament. Inside the acetabulum it is attached to the non-articular surface of the femoral head along-side the teres ligament.

The prominence on the outer side of the thigh usually referred to as the hip joint is, in reality, the *major trochanter of the femur*. The true hip joint lies several inches deeper and cannot be felt from the exterior.

The *joint capsule* is a double-mouthed sac attached around the head of the femur at one end and around the rim of the acetabulum

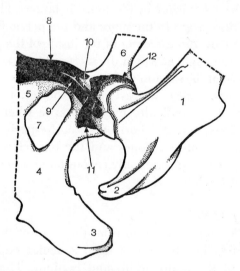

FIG. 24. Hip joint of the left side in ventral view. (After Nickel, Schummer and Seiferle.)

(1) Femur. (2) Major trochanter. (3) Tuber ischii. (4) Ischium. (5) Pubis.
(6) Ilium. (7) Obturator foramen. (8) Prepubic tendon. (9) Accessory ligament.
(10) Teres or round ligament. (11) Transverse acetabular ligament. (12) Cotyloid ligament.

at its other end. The joint permits movement in every direction although the accessory ligament limits the horse's ability to abduct its hindlimb (move the limb away from the body). This is said to make it difficult for a horse to "cow-kick" in the forward and outward direction. Nevertheless, the mule and donkey both seem able to execute this manoeuvre with comparative ease, and the ability to cow-kick is not unknown in the horse.

Most textbooks infer that the hip joint of the horse has a greater range of movement than any other joint in the body. This should be taken to refer to direction rather than extent. The accessory ligament is tensed so promptly by any inward rotation of the thigh that this movement is almost non-existent. In a horse standing squarely on all four feet the ilio-femoral angle (the angle in front of the hip joint) is 110–115 degrees, the inclination of the femur to the vertical is 80 degrees and that of the ilium 30–35 degrees to the horizontal. When the hip is flexed the femur travels forwards but in actual practice its range of movement is limited by the fact that the thigh of the horse is closely attached to the body. This is unlike the dog in which the thigh is long and the femur is free throughout the greater part of its length. Not only has the dog a long, freely operating femur, but its back is also extremely flexible and actually bends downwards during the act of galloping until the loin becomes, as it were, continuous with the thigh, thus increasing the length of the stride. The hindfeet of the horse seldom advance forward even in a fast gallop beyond a line dropped from the umbilicus (navel). Those of a greyhound shoot past the forelimbs and the hindfeet may land on the ground at the level of the point of the dog's shoulder (Fig. 42 in the Appendix).

THE FEMUR

This is a long bone, one of the heaviest and strongest in the horse's body yet like the humerus it can be shattered in the middle of a flat race by muscular incoordination. The femur acts as the medium between two very important joints, hip and stifle, and it is specially adapted for providing attachment for the large muscles which operate the upper part of the limb (Fig. 25).

It carries at its upper end a hemispherical *articular head* which fits accurately into the cavity of the acetabulum leaving a non-articular pit which gives attachment to the round and accessory ligaments. These ligaments serve to hold the head of the femur and acetabulum in close approximation. On the outer side of the upper end of the femur is the *major trochanter*. From this eminence a strong ridge descends to merge with another large prominence almost half-way down the shaft of the femur. This prominence is the *third trochanter*. These two trochanters serve for the insertion of the three major parts of the gluteal muscles, deep and middle onto the major trochanter, and superficial onto the third trochanter. On the inner surface of the shaft at the level of the third trochanter is the *minor trochanter* to which the iliopsoas muscle is attached.

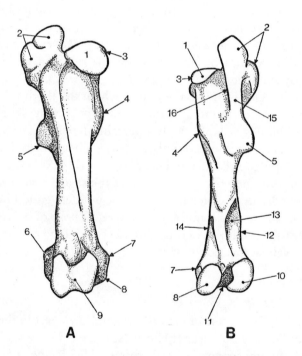

FIG. 25. Femur of the right side.
A. Anterior view. B. Posterior view.
(1) Head. (2) Major trochanter. (3) Fovea. (4) Minor trochanter. (5) Third trochanter. (6) Lateral epicondyle. (7) Medial epicondyle. (8) Medial condyle. (9) Trochlea. (10) Lateral condyle. (11) Intercondyloid fossa. (12) Lateral supracondyloid crest. (13) Supracondyloid fossa. (14) Medial supracondyloid crest. (15) Trochanteric ridge. (16) Trochanteric fossa.

Much of the *shaft of the femur* is given over to muscle attachment. Its front surface, and a great deal of both inner and outer surfaces, give origin to the three heads of the vastus muscles which comprise the bulk of the quadriceps femoris muscle group. Its posterior surface has part of the biceps femoris muscle inserting near the third trochanter and practically all of the adductor muscle from the third trochanter down.

In front, the lower end of the femur carries a double, nearly vertical, pulley-like groove known as the *trochlea*. The *inner trochlear lip* is much fuller and extends up higher than the outer, and the two converge below. Thus the trochlea provides a smooth, V-shaped groove, well reinforced with fibrocartilage to increase the depth, in which the *patella* glides up and down. On the reverse side of the lower end of the femur are the *medial* and *lateral condyles* separated by an *intercondyloid fossa*. These form the upper section of the true stifle joint articulating with the head of the tibia and with the *intra-articular fibrocartilages*. Between the lateral condyle and the trochlea is the *extensor fossa*, a depression in which the common tendon of origin of the long digital extensor muscle and the peroneus tertius muscle is attached. Above the condyles on the hind surface of the femur are both *medial* and *lateral supracondyloid ridges* giving origin to the two heads of the gastrocnemius muscle. These ridges flank the supracondyloid fossa for the origin of the superficial digital flexor muscle. *Medial* and *lateral epicondyles* are present between the condyles and the ridges of the trochlea. The medial epicondyle is the more pronounced and gives insertion to parts of both the semimembranosus and the adductor muscles.

THE TIBIA AND FIBULA

The *tibia* is a long bone extending obliquely down and back between stifle and hock joints (Fig. 26). The upper end is divided into a *tibial tuberosity*, a non-articular prominence for attachment of the patellar ligaments; while behind this on each side of the tibial head is an articular surface composed of *medial* and *lateral condyles*. The condyles are slightly concave and are separated by a sharp raised prominence, the *tibial spine*. The upper end of the tibial shaft provides attachment areas for muscles acting on the hock and digits. The most important is the deep digital flexor muscle coming from the region of the lateral condyle and the posterior surface of the shaft of the tibia (and fibula). The lateral digital extensor muscle and the anterior tibial muscle also arise from the region of the lateral condyle and the lateral surface of the shaft.

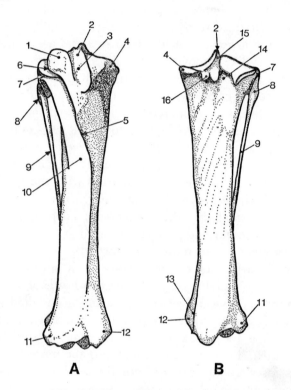

FIG. 26. Tibia and fibula of the right side.
A. Anterior view. B. Posterior view.
(1) Tibial tuberosity. (2) Tibial spine. (3) Groove for middle patellar ligament.
(4) Medial condyle. (5) Tibial crest. (6) Muscular groove. (7) Lateral condyle.
(8) Head of fibula. (9) Shaft of fibula. (10) Shaft of tibia. (11) Lateral malleolus.
(12) Medial malleolus. (13) Groove for long digital extensor. (14) Popliteal notch.
(15) Fossa for anterior cruciate ligament. (16) Tubercle for posterior cruciate
ligament.

The lower end of the tibia carries an *articular surface* composed of two deep articular grooves separated by an articular ridge. The whole articular surface is moulded accurately upon the similar ridges and grooves in the tibial tarsal bone, the bone of the hock with which it articulates. The ridges and grooves in tibia and tibial tarsal bone are set obliquely forwards and outwards. It is extremely important that this particular angle of obliquity should be exactly correct. The whole movement of the lower portion of the limb is linked up with the accuracy of the direction of these articular grooves.

The *fibula* is a much reduced long bone articulating with the outer surface of the lateral tibial condyle. It is a thin bone, not unlike a small metacarpal (splint) bone which tapers away to a point at the lower third of the tibial shaft. Between the bodies of the tibia and fibula is an elongated *interosseous space*. The lower end of the fibula is fused with the tibia forming its *lateral malleolus*.

THE STIFLE JOINT

Just as the carpus, or knee, of the horse is analogous with the human wrist, so the hock of the horse corresponds with the human ankle and the stifle joint with the human knee. The stifle contains two separate articulations, one between the tibia and femur, the femorotibial articulation; the other between the patella and the femur, the femoropatellar articulation.

(a) *The femorotibial articulation*

This joint (Figs. 27 and 28) consists of the condyles of the femur articulating with the condylar surfaces of the tibial head. These articular surfaces are not adapted to one another there only being a small area of contact centrally. Congruence of the articular surfaces is produced by the interposition of two plates of fibro-cartilage, the *menisci* or *intra-articular cartilages*. The outer edge of these crescentic cartilages are thick and convex, while the inner edge is concave, thin and translucent. The lower surface of each is flat and rests on the condylar surface of the tibia. The upper surface is concave to receive the femoral condyle.

The menisci are held in place by fibrous *meniscal ligaments*, attached to the tibial head in front of and behind the spine. The lateral meniscus also has an additional attachment posteriorly to the intercondyloid fossa of the femur (Fig. 27B). The ligaments of the joint itself, a ginglymus, are in the form of normal *medial* and *lateral collateral ligaments*. In addition, two strong fibrous cords, the *cruciate ligaments*, are situated mainly in the intercondyloid fossa, crossing each other like the letter X, and attaching tibia to femur. These ligaments do not lie in a sagittal plane but are

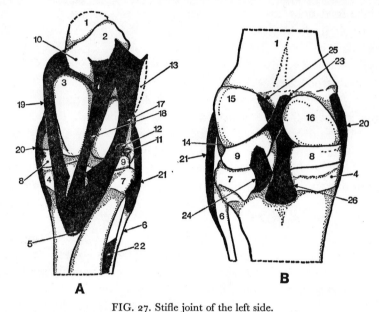

FIG. 27. Stifle joint of the left side.
A. Anterior view. B. Posterior view. (After Sisson and Grossman.)
(1) Femur. (2) Patella. (3) Medial ridge of trochlea. (4) Medial condyle of tibia. (5) Tibial tuberosity. (6) Fibula. (7) Lateral condyle of tibia. (8) Medial meniscus. (9) Lateral meniscus. (10) Accessory cartilage of patella. (11) Stump of extensor longus and peroneus tertius. (12) Stump of fascia lata. (13) Insertion of biceps femoris muscle. (14) Stump of popliteus tendon. (15) Lateral condyle of femur. (16) Medial condyle of femur. (17) Lateral patellar ligament. (18) Middle patellar ligament. (19) Medial patellar ligament. (20) Medial femorotibial ligament. (21) Lateral femorotibial ligament. (22) Interosseous ligament. (23) Femoral ligament of lateral meniscus. (24) Posterior ligament of lateral meniscus. (25) Anterior cruciate ligament. (26) Posterior cruciate ligament.

twisted slightly so that outward rotation of the leg untwists and slackens them.

The menisci presumably function to correct the disparity between the femoral condyles and the articular surfaces of the tibia, and they act also as shock absorbers. The cruciate ligaments and the collateral ligaments function to prevent overextension.

(b) *The femoropatellar articulation*

This joint occurs between the trochlea of the femur and the patella. The *patella* is a sesamoid bone and subserves essentially the same functions as the proximal sesamoids of the fetlock. It provides a mechanical advantage for the quadriceps muscle of the thigh, a stifle extensor, by removing its line of action further from the centre of rotation of the joint. The patella, although not weight bearing, also provides a compression and tension resistant element in the quadriceps femoris tendon. It transmits the muscular pull exerted upon it to the tibia through three long ligamentous cords, the *patellar ligaments* (Fig. 27A). These ligaments are inserted into the tuberosity of the head of the tibia and are palpable and visible in the living animal immediately below the patella. The *middle patellar ligament* which is the strongest of the three has a special groove on the tibial tuberosity scooped out for its reception (Fig. 26A). These ligaments are actually tendons of insertion of the quadriceps muscle mass of the thigh. The *lateral patellar ligament* also receives a strong tendon from the biceps femoris and the tensor fasciae latae muscles through the attachment to it of the fascia lata of the thigh. The middle patellar ligament is only concerned with the vastus and the rectus femoris muscle insertion. The *medial patellar ligament* is the weakest of the three and is joined also by a diffuse tendon from the gracilis and sartorius muscles of the inner side of the thigh.

The patella carries on its inner, articular surface a central vertical ridge separating two small concave areas on either side. The ridge fits into the groove on the femoral trochlea, but the lateral areas on the patella do not fit the ridges of the trochlea at all accurately. The inner, concave patellar area, like the inner trochlear ridge, is much the wider of the two and these surfaces are rendered more congruent by the curved *accessory fibrocartilage*.

MOVEMENT OF THE STIFLE JOINT

The stifle joint is a hinge joint (ginglymus) with principal movements of flexion and extension. In the normal standing position the angle behind the stifle varies from 135 to 140 degrees. Flexion of the joint is limited only by contact of the leg with the thigh. Extension of the joint is incomplete, the thigh and leg bones never come quite into the same straight line, further movement being checked by the tension of the collateral and cruciate ligaments.

During stifle flexion and extension there may be times when the patella is in danger of slipping out of its trochlear groove. This risk of patellar dislocation is reduced somewhat by *medial* and *lateral femoropatellar ligaments*. Thus in the horse it is unusual for

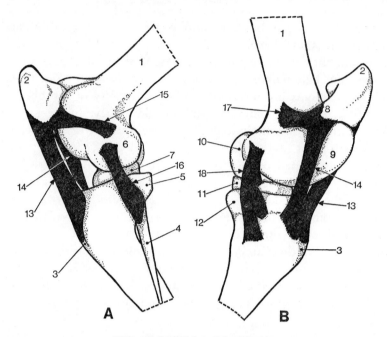

FIG. 28. Stifle joint of the left side.
A. Lateral view. B. Medial view.
(1) Femur. (2) Patella. (3) Tibial tuberosity. (4) Fibula. (5) Lateral condyle of tibia. (6) Lateral condyle of femur. (7) Lateral meniscus. (8) Accessory fibro-cartilage of the patella. (9) Medial ridge of trochlea. (10) Medial condyle of femur. (11) Medial meniscus. (12) Medial condyle of tibia. (13) Middle patellar ligament. (14) Medial patellar ligament. (15) Lateral femoropatellar ligament. (16) Lateral femorotibial ligament. (17) Medial femoropatellar ligament. (18) Medial femoro-tibial ligament.

the patella to be pulled over the rim of the trochlea either intern-ally or externally. More often it is pulled in an upward direction and hooks itself over the upper end of the inner trochlear ridge (Fig. 28B). This patellar or stifle locking mechanism occurs when the stifle joint is subjected to a degree of extension not occurring during normal locomotion. This will in effect prevent flexion of the stifle as long as the hip is flexed, since in hip flexion outward rotation of the femur occurs seating the medial patellar ligament firmly on the medial trochlear ridge. In this state stifle flexion jams the patellar ligament system on the medial trochlear ridge and fixes the stifle in position. In order to unlock this system the quadriceps femoris muscle may contract lifting the patella, while the biceps femoris muscle contracts to pull the patella laterally off the ridge. Also if the hip extends, followed by stifle extension, unlocking should occur. This process we shall see later on as being of extreme importance in the resting position of the horse. However, patellar fixation often occurs in horses with "straight" hind-legs in which inadvertent overextension and subsequent locking are likely to occur. This results in the limb being locked in full extension with the result that the hindlimb, stretched to its utmost, is carried behind the horse's body. While surgical division of the medial patellar ligament will prevent fixation, it does not correct the basic cause which is overextension of the stifle joint. Reposition requires veterinary assistance and is usually effected by applying forward traction helped by inducing the horse to make a sudden jump forward on the sound limb. This condition of patellar luxation in the upward direction is frequently encountered in colts and fillies. It may be hereditary and has been associated with certain stallions. In most cases the tendency towards involuntary patellar fixation usually lessens or disappears when the bones attain full length and growth ceases.

THE TARSUS OR HOCK

In the same way as the knee, the hock is made up of several joints (Figs. 29 and 30). However, it articulates directly with the lower end of the tibia through only a single bone, the *tibial tarsal*. The six bones comprising the tarsus are bound together tightly by ligaments. All are short bones and arranged roughly in three rows. In the upper row are the *tibial tarsal* (astragalus) and *fibular tarsal* (os calcis); in the middle row the *central tarsal* (scaphoid) alone; in the lower row the *first and second tarsals* (internal and middle cuneiforms) fused together and the *third tarsal* (external cuneiform). The *fourth tarsal* (cuboid), a six-sided bone shaped like a brick, occupies a part of both middle and lower rows being as deep as the central tarsal and third tarsal. It stands alone, directly beneath the fibular tarsal bone.

The *tibial tarsal* is an irregularly-shaped bone composed of a pulley-like articular surface or *trochlea* which conforms with that of the lower end of the tibia. This surface carries two rounded ridges and a deep groove between them. The groove is directed spirally downwards, forwards and outwards, taking nearly a half

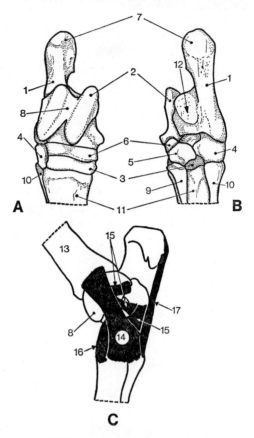

FIG. 29. Tarsus of the right side.
A. Anterior view. B. Posterior view. C. Medial view showing the main ligaments of
the hock.
(1) Fibular tarsal. (2) Tibial tarsal. (3) Third tarsal. (4) Fourth tarsal. (5) First
tarsal fused with second tarsal. (6) Central tarsal. (7) Tuber calcis. (8) Trochlea.
(9) Second metatarsal. (10) Fourth metatarsal. (11) Large metatarsal. (12) Tarsal
groove for deep flexor tendon. (13) Tibia. (14) Long medial collateral ligament.
(15) Short medial ligaments. (16) Dorsal tarsal ligaments. (17) Plantar ligament.

turn around the bone. The hindside of the bone carries four
facets for articulation with the fibular tarsal, together with some
roughened surfaces for the attachment of ligaments.

The *fibular tarsal* is the largest bone of the hock and is made up
of a body with a large upstanding process, the *tuber calcis* (the
point of the hock, equivalent to the human heel). The body is
moulded on the posterior surface of the tibial tarsal and its

articular facets, and has on its lower part a strong, inwardly projecting process, the *sustentaculum tali*. The lower surface of this projection forms a groove with the main body of the bone, the *tarsal groove* (Fig. 29B), for the tendon of the deep digital flexor muscle. The tuber calcis has an almost flat outer surface and a concave inner surface which enters into the formation of the

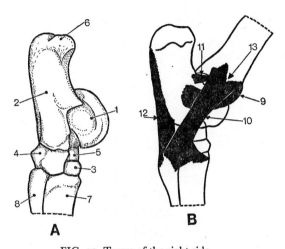

FIG. 30. Tarsus of the right side.
A. Lateral view. B. Lateral view showing the main ligaments of the hock.
(1) Tibial tarsal. (2) Fibular tarsal. (3) Third tarsal. (4) Fourth tarsal. (5) Central tarsal. (6) Tuber calcis. (7) Large metatarsal. (8) Fourth metatarsal. (9) Short lateral ligaments. (10) Long lateral collateral ligament. (11) Ligament between tibial and fibular tarsals. (12) Plantar ligament. (13) Groove for lateral extensor tendon.

tarsal groove. The tuber calcis forms a lever arm for attachment of the extensor muscles of the hock, especially the gastrocnemius and the tarsal tendon of the biceps femoris and semitendinosus muscles. The tendon of the superficial digital flexor muscle also caps the point of the hock and attaches to its hind surface. The outer lateral face is roughened and non-articular and carries a prominent blunt tuberosity. The inner surface carries a wide, shallow pit. These both give attachment to the ligaments that bind the joint together (Figs. 29C and 30B).

The *central tarsal* is a flattened bone, slightly concave on top for articulation with the tibial tarsal. It occupies the whole of the central row, apart from the fourth tarsal which has the same depth as that of the central and third tarsals combined.

The *third tarsal*, the flat bone of the lowest row, much resembles the central tarsal but is smaller and more triangular in shape. The smallest of all, the fused first and second tarsals, situated on the inner side of the hock, is roughly triangular, with its base at the rear and its apex pointing downwards and forwards.

Various bones of the hock provide attachment for muscles besides those attaching to the tuber calcis. Therefore the hock flexors are inserted onto the first tarsal (anterior tibial muscle) and third, fourth and fibular tarsal bones (peroneus tertius muscle). Both of these muscles also attach to the upper end of the large metatarsal bone.

The bones of the hock can be palpated by delicate fingers if the skin is not too thick, or the hock too coarse. This exercise is of great value in the diagnosis of *spavin*. True spavin is a bone inflammation which commences usually on the inner side of the hock near the head of the metatarsal bone and extends into the fused first and second tarsals, and sometimes the central tarsal. It produces ulceration of the articular surfaces with deposition of new bony deposits on the external edges, a healing process. This interferes with the complete flexion of the joint and causes lameness. The lameness is most pronounced when the horse comes out of the stable but diminishes with exercise. The condition is believed to be hereditary, but whether it is the pathological condition which is transmitted, the conformation, or the quality of the bone, is still not certain.

MOVEMENT OF THE HOCK JOINT

For all practical purposes the hock is a ginglymus moving in only one direction, since practically the whole movement takes place between the tibia and tibial tarsal bone. In fact more movement takes place between these two bones in the horse than in most other animals and less between the tibial tarsal and central tarsal. Movement between the remaining bones is very slight. Lateral movement is prevented by the structure of the joint surfaces, although the overall movement is in an oblique direction.

The joint capsule is thin in front but extremely thick on the underside forming the *plantar ligament* (Figs. 29 and 30). This ligament, which is cartilaginous in part, forms a smooth surface for the deep digital flexor tendon. The capsule also gives rise to the *sub-tarsal check ligament* which unites lower down with the deep flexor tendon.

In the normal standing position the angle in front of the hock is approximately 150 degrees. Like the elbow and stifle this is the middle position of the joint and the articular surfaces are in maximum contact. Complete extension is prevented by the *collateral ligaments*; flexion is checked only by contact of the metatarsus with the leg.

The hock joint is one of the hardest working structures in the horse's body. Much of the animal's activity is centred around its ability to flex and extend the hock joint rapidly and rhythmically with perfect timing. The stifle and hock joints are synchronized in their movements by virtue of the ligaments and muscles which control them. When the stifle flexes the hock flexes; when the hock extends the stifle extends. One does not function independently of the other on account of the tendinous bands in front of and behind the limb. These are the peroneus tertius and the superficial digital flexor muscles respectively, extending from the lower part of the femur to the tarsus and metatarsus. It follows, therefore, that a horse with a straight stifle carries a straight hock, and vice versa. Thus an animal standing squarely on all four feet possesses hocks as flexed as its stifles. This would mean that the hocks, if excessively flexed, would be placed far back and a line dropped from the tuber ischii to the ground would not lie, as it should, in a straight line with the posterior edge of the hindlimb from hock to heel. It would pass down the side of the hock or, in an extreme case, even in front of it. This implies that such a horse must possess a particularly long tibia. Although such a combination is regarded nowadays in most pedigree dog breeds as essential to winning prizes in exhibition, it would be regarded by most horse breeders with far less satisfaction. Dog breeders maintain that this type of "angulation" enables a dog to propel its body more easily by use of the hindlimbs, in spite of the fact that every racehorse trainer, and every man who races greyhounds, is aware that greater speed is derived from a straighter hindlimb. The reason is that both horse and dog cover the ground faster by a series of rapid short strides than by fewer long strides.

The remaining portions of the hindlimb greatly resemble those of the forelimb. The hindfoot is narrower and more upright than the fore, but in each case the outer surface of the sole and wall is a little more convex than the inner aspect which is flatter. The sole of the hindfoot is also a little more concave than that of the forefoot.

PART TWO

THE SURFACE OF THE HORSE

This portion of the book should be read with frequent reference to Part One. It may well be that some slight repetition will occur in places, but in order to make matters clear this has sometimes been necessary. The majority of established horsemen and regular riders will be acquainted with most of the surface features depicted in Chart Two. Those who are not should study these preferably by comparing the chart with a living horse before proceeding further. It is possible, however, that a few of the established horsemen, including some of those who judge, may have a rather vague idea as to what they would find beneath the surface features and variations in contour if they removed the skin which covers them. Further study of the bony structures discussed in Part One combined with the information given in this section should provide a more complete picture. This information should then be useful and profitable whenever they wish to sum up the points, good and bad, of any horse brought before them.

Many of us are quite content if we can look at a car and listen to it ticking over, but we get more enjoyment out of driving it, and a far greater sense of security, if we find out how it is made and what makes it tick. This applies to the horse just as much as to the car.

The surface of the horse's body should be studied not only with the eyes but also with the finger-tips. A blind-man possessed of a delicate sense of touch may have a better understanding of whether two limbs, two feet or two surfaces are identical, or how and to what extent they differ. Moreover, by touch alone, a blind man can detect differences too small to be seen by a man possessing normal vision. Veterinary surgeons, however, use both eyes and fingers, and when diagnosing bone conditions or the state of tendons or ligaments, first employ vision and then confirm their findings by examining and comparing suspected parts and sound parts with the finger-tips.

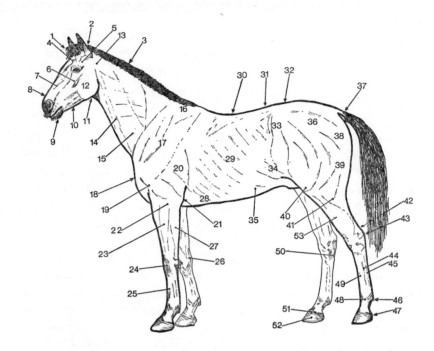

CHART TWO. The surface of the horse.

(1) Forelock. (2) Poll. (3) Mane. (4) Forehead. (5) Temporal muscle in temporal fossa. (6) Facial crest. (7) Nasal bone. (8) Nasal peak. (9) Prominence of chin. (10) Mandibular ramus. (11) Larynx. (12) Masseter muscle. (13) Wing of atlas. (14) Jugular furrow. (15) Brachiocephalic muscle. (16) Withers. (17) Scapular spine. (18) Point of the shoulder. (19) Deltoid tuberosity. (20) Triceps long head. (21) Point of the elbow. (22) Site of elbow joint. (23) Extensor muscles of knee and digit. (24) Knee. (25) Metacarpal bones. (26) Accessory carpal. (27) Flexor muscles of knee and digit. (28) Pectoral muscles. (29) Thoracic rib-cage. (30) Saddle. (31) Loin. (32) Croup (tuber sacrale). (33) Haunch (tuber coxae). (34) Flank. (35) Belly. (36) Quarter. (37) Tail head or dock. (38) Seat bone (tuber ischii). (39) Hamstring muscles. (40) Stifle joint. (41) Gaskin or second thigh. (42) Achilles tendon. (43) Point of hock. (44) Suspensory ligament. (45) Flexor tendons. (46) Ergot. (47) Heel. (48) Fetlock. (49) Metatarsal bones. (50) Chestnut. (51) Coronary band. (52) Horny wall of foot. (53) Extensors of digit.

THE SKIN

Not everyone gets an opportunity to skin a dead horse. It is an experience which provides a great deal of information as to the degree of thickness of the skin over various parts of the body, together with more as to the tightness or slackness of the skin itself and its attachments to the body. There may be little connective tissue in parts, while at others the fibrous tissue of the subcutis joining the skin to the underlying structures may be sponge-like and loose. Wherever danger of injury to the body is great the skin is correspondingly thicker. Hence that covering the back, loins, quarters and limbs is the thickest, even as much as a quarter of an inch over the loins. That covering the face, muzzle and flanks, and the inner side of the limbs, on the other hand, may be little thicker than brown paper. Nevertheless, even the thinnest skin possesses very great tensile strength. In fact in most parts of the body a single hook penetrating sound skin will enable the body to be dragged across the floor of a slaughterhouse without tearing the skin.

The skin is least thick in the thoroughbred and Arab, and thickest in the draught breeds. The thickness of the skins of ponies varies according to whether they retain their true type or have been crossed with thoroughbreds. When picked up between finger and thumb the feel of the skin can be misleading, since the skin may carry a variable amount of subcutaneous fat attached to it. In a horse in good but not necessarily in 'hard' condition, a hand placed flat upon the skin covering the ribs may be moved from side to side, the skin gliding over the underlying structures on account of the presence of the fat. In a thin horse the skin will feel firm and practically immovable as though it were glued to the ribs. 'Hidebound' horses may be suffering from loss or absence of fat, but in some debilitated horses, particularly when suffering from the effects of intestinal worms, the skin conditions may arise from dehydration and the consequent lack of fluid in and beneath the skin.

The skin consists of two principal layers, the superficial *epidermis* and the deeper *dermis*. Sensory nerve ramifications, blood vessels and glands (both sweat and sebaceous) are present in the dermis. The epidermis on the other hand is avascular with its outer layers being formed of dying and dead cells which eventually are cast off. The deepest epidermal layer, the *stratum germinativum*, is responsible for epidermal regeneration to compensate for the loss by desquamation of the outer epidermal layer. The generative layer also contains *melanin*, a black or brown pigment which absorbs violet radiation and protects the skin and body from the effect of excessive sunlight.

The epidermis is perforated by the passage of hairs and their follicles and by the ducts of glands. Its principal function is to prevent the penetration of liquids through the skin, partly owing to the deposition of fatty secretion from the sebaceous glands on to its surface. Important subsidiary functions performed by the skin are those of temperature regulation, aided by the hairs and sweat glands, and excretion, through both types of glands. Sensory perception is an important attribute of skin and some areas are far more sensitive than others. Parts such as the lips and muzzle used for making contact with food and near-by objects, are provided with long feeler hairs. These hairs are connected to a highly sensitive root provided with a number of sensory nerves. Horses use these hairs a good deal especially when feeding both from the ground and from a manger. Mares muzzle their foals making use of these sensory hairs and it is likely they recognize their own foals in this way as much as by their sense of smell.

THE SKIN MUSCULATURE

The skin is attached to the underlying parts by subcutaneous connective tissue containing elastic fibres and fat, the *subcutis*. In some parts of the body, notably the neck and back, tenseness of the skin is normal owing to the presence in the subcutis of a thin voluntary muscle layer, the *cutaneous muscle*, intimately adherent in great part to the skin. The cutaneous muscle has only a limited attachment to the skeleton. The part of the muscle in the neck attaches to the cariniform cartilage of the sternum. The abdominal part of the muscle covers a large part of the body behind the shoulder and arm having attachments to the medial tuberosity of the humerus in front and the patella above the stifle at the back. On contraction the muscle can twitch the skin in order to rid the greater part of the body of flies, dust, dirt and other irritants, something one will often have observed when the horse rises from its bed in the morning. The cutaneous muscle being adherent to the skin may produce shivering by very rapid contractions which raise the local temperature by bringing more warm blood to the cold surface. In a few places, notably the face, the cutaneous muscle is modified and the skin is less adherent to it.

THE SKIN GLANDS

The *sebaceous glands* are minute structures freely distributed throughout the whole of the horse's skin in close association with the hair roots. The *sebum* is not a true secretion but an oily semiliquid material which solidifies on exposure to the air. It renders the skin pliable and waterproof. It also contains substances which are converted into vitamin D by the action of sunlight. Horses which habitually lick one another at pasture are not only deriving salt from the other horse's skin but also precursors of vitamin D which they swallow.

The sebaceous glands are remarkable for the fact that they do not actually secrete the sebum but deliver it as the result of the destruction of degenerated and debilitated gland cells. Their nutrition has been cut off by the rapid growth of the outer layers of cells. These squeeze the dying and dead cells towards the centre of the follicle and then into the duct through which the sebum is expelled to the surface. Spread thinly over the individual hairs, sebum is responsible for the gloss of the coat. It can be spread to the best advantage by regular careful grooming.

The horse is one of the few hairy animals in which sweating occurs over almost the whole body surface. The exception in its case is the skin of the legs. The frothy sweat which accumulates on the legs after a long gallop has trickled down from the belly and the insides of the elbows and thighs. Sweating in animals which possess the necessary apparatus is a continuous process and normally evaporation takes place, except during the fastest gaits, as rapidly as the sweat is produced. It has been estimated that, within certain limits, the sweat secretion of a horse grazing out of doors in ordinary Summer weather and choosing its own pace averages 14 lb. of fluid during each 24 hours without any visible dampness of the body surface. When horses are galloped the output of sweat and resulting loss of tissue fluid is much greater than this amount. Sweating is influenced by external temperature, the degree of humidity (though this may influence visible more than actual sweating), the length of the coat, the degree of excitement, the environment, whether the horse is at leisure or at work, and by the pace. A horse may sweat, however, when it is hot or cold. In the latter case excessive sweating arises from a nervous stimulation of the adrenal glands causing them to pour out more adrenalin into the blood stream which stimulates particular areas of the brain. It is therefore this excessive secretion of adrenalin dependent upon an anxiety state which causes a horse to sweat prior to a race, even on a fairly cold day.

Horse sweat also contains protein substances derived from the blood, possibly explaining why horses that sweat too freely lose weight, and also why, after drying off, it mats the hair. It also leaves upon the hair surface, and upon the skin, crystals or other deposits of the mineral substances it contains.

Illness in horses can result from oversweating or undersweating. Horses exported from temperate to tropical climates may lose the ability to sweat and may develop a condition known as 'drycoat'. If returned to the cooler climate recovery occurs automatically within a few weeks. It would appear that in affected horses the sweat glands lose their ability to become stimulated by the presence of adrenalin in the blood stream. Such animals are useless for racing and if galloped may collapse from heart failure.

THE HAIR

Hair covers practically the entire body surface. However, more hair is carried over the parts of the skin exposed to direct sunlight than on the less exposed areas such as the inner surface of the ears, the inner side of the thighs, the perineum and the external genitalia in both sexes.

The skin carries *permanent hair* in the mane and tail, in the 'feathering' of certain heavy breeds and in the eyelashes and long hairs of the muzzle. Permanent hair goes on growing indefinitely regardless of the temperature changes. The bulk of the hair covering the body is *temporary hair* which is shed and changed for a new growth of hair in spring and autumn, in preparation for the summer and winter coats. The temporary hair covering consists of closely placed patches of long hairs, 27–30 to the square inch. These tend to hide the undercoat from view. This is made up of densely packed finer and shorter hairs, as many as 4300 to the square inch of skin.

The hairs play a prominent role in temperature regulation. The skin itself is a bad conductor of heat and especially so when left ungroomed to become dirty, a feature usually taken full advantage of before turning horses out to grass. Hair responds in automatic fashion to heat and cold. In a cold atmosphere the hairs tend to rise and form a blanket imprisoning a layer of warm air. In warm weather the coat lies flat, but the skin may be cooled by the evaporation of sweat from its surface. The rise and fall of the hair is due partly to the action of the cutaneous muscle lying beneath the skin, but mainly to the reflexes of the tiny involuntary muscle fibres attached to each hair follicle in the dermis. In the horse, hair raising is activated by cold but not by fear or anger, as in the cat and dog and some higher animals.

The deciding factor in coat casting is principally temperature, but the number of hours of daylight is also important. If horses are kept in artificial heating in winter, as they frequently were in bygone days while on long sea voyages, they shed their winter coats within a matter of days however low the temperature may have been outside. Similarly under conditions of cold the coat grows rapidly and to a greater length. Coat casting is seldom so rapid that the animal becomes bald. As a rule the new coat is growing underneath the old and it tends to push the latter off. Hard keep delays coat casting, while good feeding and the provision of oils and essential vitamins will hasten the process. Mares shabby in coat will seldom conceive and may fail to come into season until the new jacket has made its appearance. Crossing indigenous ponies with thoroughbreds or Arabs produces a change in the type of coat. Such animals may become unable to withstand winter conditions on moors and hills, or even in open pasture sometimes.

In 1930 the Royal College of Veterinary Surgeons published a report by a subcommittee set up by the Council in 1928 to prepare a system of description of colours, markings, etc., of horses for identification purposes. In October 1954 the Council set up a committee to reconsider this report and approved a system superseding the previous one. A copy of this can be obtained from

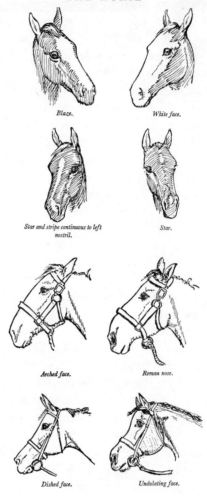

Blaze.   *White face.*

Star and stripe continuous to left nostril.   *Star.*

Arched face.   *Roman nose.*

Dished face.   *Undulating face.*

FIG. 31. Eight head drawings contributed by Mr. A. C. Shuttleworth, M.V.Sc., F.R.C.V.S.

The Secretary, Royal College of Veterinary Surgeons, 32 Belgrave Square, London.

THE HEAD

After one has become familiar with the arrangement of the bones of the skeleton (Chart One) one may study the various parts of the external surface of the body referring back to Part One, when required, for further details of the bony structure lying beneath any outstanding feature. Firstly let us take a general look over the horse comparing it with Chart Two and with Figs. 31 and 32. After this we will consider the various external features in greater detail and discuss the structures which, lying beneath the skin, bring about changes in the contour of the body. The first thing we shall require will be a horse, the thinner the better, in order that salient features will not be disguised by the presence of an excessive amount of subcutaneous fat.

Commencing at the *poll* note the *mane* with the *forelock* growing a little way down over the *forehead* from a triangular portion of skin which extends slightly in front of the bases of the ears with its apex at the lowest point. The mane extends back to the commencement of the withers. Unattended it may grow a foot or more in length, particularly in mountain ponies and heavy horses. Sometimes it falls always to one side of the neck, in others it divides and passes over each side. In saddle horses it is usually cut short (hogged), or it may be pulled and maintained at a length of a few inches either hanging free or braided.

The *ears* which should be erect, actively mobile and not too large, are carried closely on either side of the prominence at the highest point of the skull, the *external occipital protuberance of the nuchal crest*. The portion of the skull at the front and upper part of the head reaching from the nuchal crest down to the level of the temporal fossa is the *cranium*. This surrounds and encloses the brain (Fig. 34). The upper surface of the cranium, in front of the poll, has a midline *interparietal crest* which shallows in front and diverges into the two *external parietal crests* which pass towards the orbits. The front wall of the cranial cavity forms part of the walls and floor of the *frontal sinus* (Fig. 2). This large cavity lies beneath the lower part of the forehead. and its position, depth and extent can be judged from Figs. 2 and 3 in Part One. You can also map this hollow space by tapping with your knuckles on the forehead between the eyes, comparing the sound with that coming from the surrounding parts. The large frontal sinus is an air cavity designed to allow widening of the skull without adding to its weight. It enables the head to carry a wider upper jaw with additional space for both teeth and nasal passages. Otherwise the frontal sinuses, of which there are two divided by a midline septum, play little part in respiratory air-flow, although they do fill during expiration.

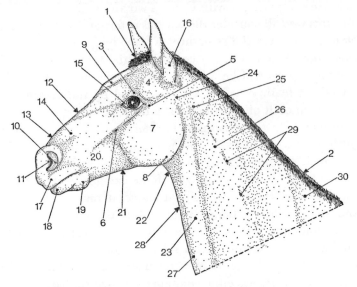

FIG. 32. Landmarks on the surface of the head and neck.
(1) Forelock on forehead. (2) Mane. (3) Supraorbital process of frontal. (4) Temporal fossa. (5) Zygomatic arch. (6) Facial crest. (7) Masseter muscle. (8) Angle of mandible. (9) Frontal bone. (10) Outer wing of nostril. (11) Inner wing of nostril. (12) Nasal bone. (13) Nasal peak. (14) Nasomaxillary notch. (15) Nictitating membrane. (16) Conchal cartilage. (17) Upper lip. (18) Lower lip. (19) Prominence of chin. (20) Cheek. (21) Mandibular ramus. (22) Larynx. (23) Jugular furrow. (24) Parotid gland. (25) Wing of atlas. (26) Brachiocephalic muscle. (27) Sternohyoid muscle. (28) Trachea. (29) Transverse processes of cervical vertebrae. (30) Trapezius muscle.

The *temporal fossa* is, from outward appearance, a depression on either side of the forehead immediately behind each *supraorbital process of the frontal bone*. This process or bridge actually completes the circle of bone forming the *orbit* which contains and protects the eyeball. The supraorbital process is quite visible through the skin of the forehead and it can be palpated throughout its length. The upper end of the lower jawbone (the *coronoid process*) moves freely within the temporal fossa together with a pad of fat. Also located in the fossa is a slightly raised area overlying the *temporal muscle*, lying on the surface of the cranium in front of the base of the ears.

The lower border of the temporal fossa, and of the orbit, is delimited by a ridge of bone, observable at the outer corner of the eye, lying beneath the skin and running slightly upwards. It causes a visible bulging of the skin at this point and feels very hard to the touch. This is the *zygomatic arch* which completes the closing of the orbit and unites the supraorbital process of the frontal bone with the outer surface of the cranium. The zygomatic arch expands dorsally just before reaching the cranial wall, the expansion lying above the level of the *jaw* (*temporomandibular*) *joint* (Fig. 1). The zygoma is continued forwards in a straight line onto the side of the face as the rather prominent *zygomatic ridge* or *facial crest*. The arch and ridge give attachment to the powerful *masseter muscle*. This muscle lies beneath the wide semicircular area of skin extending from below the eye to the curved hinder edge of the lower jaw bone where it attaches to the outer face of the mandible (Figs. 32 and 35). The temporal and masseter muscles work in collaboration in raising the lower jaw and therefore closing the mouth.

The *orbit* of the horse containing the *eyeball* is not placed frontally as in man but lies on either side of a wide forehead (Fig. 3). The eyes therefore are directed a little obliquely and do not converge upon objects lying straight ahead without some effort on the part of the horse. The angle of optical divergence in the horse (the angle at which two lines of vision cross the body axis) is $35\frac{1}{2}$ degrees, which permits a 71 degree binocular field. Thus the two eyes see, by one means or another, through a range of 215 degrees. It will be recognized, however, that taking into consideration the position of the horse's eyes in its head, and the fact that it carries a relatively wide forehead (wider in heavy draught horses than in thoroughbreds), the horse must experience some difficulty in persuading its two eyes to converge simultaneously upon an object lying a short distance ahead. The forehead of a heavyweight hunter is much wider than that of a thoroughbred. As a result the eyes of the latter are closer together and the possibility of both eyes converging and focussing upon an object some little distance ahead is greater. In any event it sees no object in front of it quite clearly using its two eyes together unless the distance of the object from the eyes exceeds 4 feet. Horses, unlike ourselves, do not have a spherical eyeball but have one which is somewhat flattened from front to back. They also have the additional complication that the lower part of the eyeball is more flattened than the upper part. Therefore the retinal layer of the eye (upon which the image is focused) is closer to the lens at its bottom than it is at its top part. The retina is arranged on a slope or ramp. This type of retina means that both near objects on the ground, and far ones on the horizon can be in focus at the same time. This was obviously of extreme importance throughout the evolution of the horses. When grazing with head down, horses would have been exposed to predators, but would have been able to see and focus on both grass and approaching carnivores. Although the horse has a reasonably well developed ciliary muscle the lens is non-elastic, suggesting that focusing is not brought about by the same mechanism as in man. In your own eye this ciliary muscle alters the shape of an elastic lens in order to focus the image on the retina. The horse must utilize movements of the head, either up or down, in order to bring the image onto that part of the retina at the right distance to ensure sharpness of the image. It is probably aided in this by movements back and forth of the lens as a whole brought about by the ciliary muscles. It is easy to tell when a horse is actually looking straight ahead with two eyes simultaneously because the two ears will be pricked sharply forward and the head will be held fairly high with the line of the forehead and nasal bones almost vertically placed. However, at any other time than when looking directly ahead each of the horse's eyes will discern a different picture of objects situated laterally. This is an important factor since when jumping it is imperative that its gaze should be concentrated on what lies ahead and not on what is going on in other directions. The horse approaching a jump should have freedom to hold its head in the position which enables it to view the jump to the best advantage.

In addition the horse carries a wide muzzle which obscures the view of objects below eye level. It is therefore unable to see any-thing below this level from the time its head is 4 feet from the jump. This accounts for some proportion of horses which so frequently gallop almost to the jump and make a frantic effort to pull up in time to avoid a crash. The average horse has therefore to view the jump from the start of the run-up, estimate the distance or number of strides to the point of take-off, and having reached it, jump blind! This applies to many show jumpers, but less so to racehorses which usually take-off over a hurdle when considerably more than 4 feet from it.

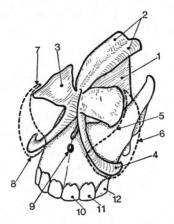

FIG. 33. Nasal cartilages and premaxillary bones.
(1) Septal cartilage (internasal septum). (2) Pareital cartilages. (3) Lamina of alar cartilage. (4) Cornu of alar cartilage. (5) Position of medial wing of nostril. (6) Position of lateral wing of nostril. (7) Superior commissure of nostril. (8) Inferior commissure of nostril. (9) Incisive foramen. (10) Central incisor teeth. (11) Lateral incisor tooth. (12) Corner incisor tooth.

THE NOSTRILS AND NASAL CAVITY

The *nostril,* the entrance to the nasal chamber, is a large somewhat oval opening bounded on either side by the *wings (alae) of the nostril* (Fig. 33). These wings meet above and below the nostril to form the *commissures,* the upper being narrow, the lower wide and rounded. Comma-shaped *alar cartilages* support the nostril wings. These cartilages are movably articulated by fibrous tissue to the *septal cartilage* of the nose which passes longitudinally down the centre line of the nasal passages. The cartilages of the wings provide the necessary support for the rim of the nostrils and prevent them collapsing and closing the nostril during inspiration. The outer wing of the nostril is concave throughout its length, but the inner wing while concave below forms a convex projection near its upper end. This prominence of the inner wing together with an alar fold passing back from it partially divides the nostril into upper and lower parts. If a finger be introduced into the nostril upwards from below the superior commissure, it will enter the upper division. This is a blind pouch extending back for some 4 inches to the *nasomaxillary notch* (Fig. 1). The pouch or "false nostril' is lined by a continuation of the skin (mainly hairless) of the face and not by mucous membrane which covers the inner surface of the nasal passages. The septal cartilage itself extends beyond the apices of the nasal bones by about 2 inches, and gives rise to narrow *parietal cartilages* one on either side. Near the nostrils these plates become wider and almost fill in the nasomaxillary notch in the bony wall of the nasal cavity.

If you open the nostril wide with your fingers and look onto the floor of the nostril about 2 inches from the lower commissure, you will see a small circular hole which gives the impression that a piece of skin had been punched out. This is the lower opening of the *nasolachrymal duct* through which tears drain from the eye to the nose. Just beyond this opening you will see that the skin which has turned round the edge of the nostril wing is replaced by pink mucous membrane which lines the nasal cavities.

Muscular action on the cartilages permits the nostrils to dilate and contract. The nostrils also expand or become dilated by the forcible expiration of air during the act of snorting.

The *nasal bones* are bilateral and triangular in shape with their bases uniting with the *frontal* and *lachrymal bones*, while their apices form the sharp, pointed *nasal peak* (Fig. 1). The two bones lie side by side and in the young animal are mainly united by cartilaginous material which becomes converted into bone during adult life. Each is convex from side to side on its outer surface and concave on its inner. The nasal bones form the roof of the entire nasal passage. Together with the maxillary bones which form the walls, and the hard palate which forms the floor, the nasal bones enclose the closely rolled, thin *turbinate bones*, two superimposed on either side (Figs. 2 and 34). One pair is separated from the other by the mainly cartilaginous *nasal septum* which divides the nasal chambers into two compartments.

THE EYES AND EYELIDS

The *upper* and *lower eyelids* surround and enclose the *palpebral fissure*, a straight slit when the eyelids are closed, but ovoid or elliptical with its long axis directed upwards and outwards when the eye is open. The eyelids act as movable curtains protecting the front of the eye, the upper being larger and thicker than the lower. Opening and closing of the eye is performed by the upper eyelid while the lower lid remains more or less stationary.

The outer surface of each lid is formed from a continuation of the skin of the face, covered by short hairs. The lower lid also has some long tactile bristles. The upper lid carries a number of thick stiff *eyelashes* arranged in four rows. The lashes cross each other like a trellis but do not interlace. The lower lid carries only a few thin, straggly eyelashes. In both lids most of the lashes emerge from the centres of the lids and few from near the extremities.

The inner surface of each lid is lined by a thin, moist, sensitive membrane known as the *conjunctiva*, and is moulded so as to move freely over the eyeball. The conjunctiva is continuous with the outer surface of the *cornea*, the transparent window at the front of the eye. However, the corneal conjunctiva is a layer of extreme delicacy, only being one cell in thickness, and intimately associated with the cornea. By lifting the lids slightly, away from the surface of the eyeball, about 40–50 dots can be seen running the length of the inner surface of the lids. These are the *Meibomian* or *tarsal glands* which secrete an oily substance onto the edges of the lids. Tears are produced continuously from the *lachrymal gland* and pass over the surface of the eye to clean it. Normally these tears drain away down the *nasolachrymal duct* into the nose. The coating of oil from the Meibomian glands along the edges of the lids prevents the overspilling of tears onto the surface of the face.

The stiffness of the lids, more marked in the upper, is due to the inclusion between the skin and the conjunctiva of each of a strip of fibrous tissue, densest along the free edge of the lid.

There is a third eyelid, the *membrana nictitans*, which lies at the inner angle of the eye with its free edge just visible. It consists of a thin, flexible, more or less T-shaped cartilage covered in front by the conjunctiva. It passes across the eye if a little pressure is placed upon the eyeball through partly closed lids. It is not operated directly by a muscle, as the foregoing statement has implied. The stem of the T-shaped cartilage is embedded in a pad of fat which lies in the orbit by the side of the eyeball. The cartilage pushes the nictitating membrane over the eye each time pressure on the eyeball squeezes the fat outwards. The membrane thus acts as a shield as well as in the manner of a screen-wiper, lifting foreign materials off the sensitive cornea. It must be understood also, that the eye retracts automatically into its socket whenever it is stimulated by pain or is threatened from the outside. This is effected by contraction of the *retractor muscle of the eye* which passes from the bone in the depths of the orbit to the back of the eyeball surrounding the optic nerve like a sheath. Contraction of this muscle pulls the eye back into the socket pressing it against the fat pad which causes the third eyelid to cover the cornea. In cases of tetanus (lockjaw) when the retractor muscle is involved in the general muscular contraction, the third eyelid remains raised and almost covering the eyeball. This is one of the earliest signs of impending tetanus.

The *lachrymal gland* lies within the orbit between the underside of the supraorbital process and the eyball above the outer corner of the eye. Several ducts open from the gland into the *conjunctival sac*. Tears are shed and pass across the surface of the eyeball towards a pair of *lachrymal ducts* situated close behind the free edge of the eyelids at the inner corner of the eye. The ducts empty into the *nasolachrymal duct* buried partly in the outer wall of the frontal sinus and nasal cavity, passing forward and downward to open in the floor of the nostril. It can be seen as a clean-cut orifice by dilating the nostril wings as noticed earlier.

Looking at the eye itself, or as much of it as is normally visible, we can first observe the cornea in the front of the eyeball through which the light passes. In the horse it is not circular but oval, being wider in its transverse diameter. It is fitted into the white outer layer of the eye, the *sclerotic coat (sclera)*, just as a watchglass fits into the case of a watch. Through the cornea the pigmented *iris*, the curtain of the eye, is visible. It is usually dark brown, sometimes nearly black, but in some odd coloured horses it may be partly white. A variable aperture is located in the centre of the iris known as the *pupil*. In horses over 4 years old it is oval, but in younger horses it is usually rounded. At the upper border of the pupil note several black hanging bodies with probably a few more projecting upwards from the lower border, the *corpora nigra*. In some horses these are so numerous that they appear to occlude the pupil. They undoubtedly act in some way to cut down the light entering the eye, but their real purpose is a little obscure.

THE EARS

Each *ear* comprises three compartments of which only the *external ear* is visible. The *middle* and *internal ears* are contained within the

petrous temporal bone which lies laterally in the posterior end
of the skull, one on either side (Fig. 1). The middle ear contains
the *tympanum* or *ear drum*, a thin elastic membrane situated between
the external and middle ears. Sound vibrations cause the diaphragm to vibrate, the vibrations being transmitted to three small
bones within the cavity of the middle ear which are linked
together. These in turn transmit the vibrations to the fluid within
the inner ear.

The skin covering the outer surface of the external ear is hairy;
the inner surface carries little hair apart from some along its
edges. Support for the external ear is provided by three separate
cartilages lying between the two layers of skin. The main, *conchal
cartilage* is somewhat trumpet shaped. Its outer orifice is elliptical
with margins meeting above and below at acute angles. (Fig. 32).
The conchal cartilage is freely movable and capable of elevation
and depression. It can also turn forwards, outwards or backwards,
towards the direction of a sound. At its lower end the conchal
cartilage becomes a complete tube where it overlaps the ring-
shaped *annular cartilage*. This surrounds the *external auditory meatus*,
a ring of bone jutting out from the temporal bone and leading
to the tympanum. The third cartilage the *scutiform*, is irregularly
quadrilateral in shape and lies beneath the skin of the forehead
over the temporal muscles. It helps to keep the ear erect by acting
as an area of attachment for muscles of the external ear (Fig. 35).
Between the skin and cartilages run a number of veins, arteries
and nerves. Some of the vessels are visible through the skin of the
ear in most horses, especially thoroughbreds.

THE LIPS, MOUTH AND TONGUE

The *mouth* or *oral cavity* (Fig. 34) is subdivided into two parts by
the teeth and jaws. The space outside the teeth is enclosed by the
lips and cheeks, the mouth cavity proper lying internal to the
teeth. When the teeth are in contact the two parts still communicate through the *interdental spaces* and the spaces behind the last
molar teeth.

The *lips* are two musculomembranous folds joining near the
first cheek tooth. The upper lip is rounded and moulded over the
incisor teeth. It is wide and fleshy and has a shallow median furrow
or philtrum. It carries on the surface of its skin a number of long

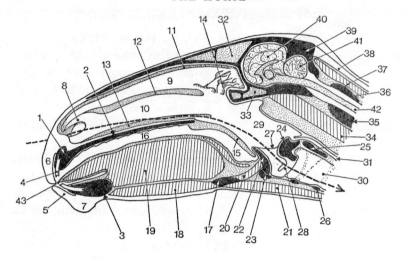

FIG. 34. Diagrammatic sagittal section of the head.
(1) Premaxilla. (2) Hard palate. (3) Mandible. (4) Incisor tooth. (5) Lower lip.
(6) Upper lip. (7) Prominence of chin. (8) Alar fold. (9) Dorsal turbinate. (10) Ventral turbinate. (11) Dorsal nasal meatus. (12) Middle nasal meatus. (13) Ventral nasal meatus. (14) Ethmoturbinates. (15) Soft palate. (16) Oral cavity. (17) Hyoid bone. (18) Geniohyoid muscle. (19) Genioglossus muscle. (20) Hyo-epiglottic muscle. (21) Sternohyoid muscle. (22) Epiglottic cartilage. (23) Thyroid cartilage. (24) Arytenoid cartilage. (25) Cricoid cartilage. (26) Tracheal ring. (27) Glottic margin. (28) Vocal cord. (29) Nasopharynx. (30) Trachea. (31) Oesophagus. (32) Frontal sinus. (33) Sphenoid sinus. (34) Rectus capitis ventralis muscle. (35) Ventral arch of atlas. (36) Dorsal arch of atlas. (37) Rectus capitis dorsalis muscle. (38) Ligamentum nuchae. (39) Occiput. (40) Cerebral hemisphere. (41) Cerebellum. (42) Spinal cord. (43) Tip of tongue. The broken line indicates the direction of air flow into the lungs.

'feeler' hairs. The upper lip is so relatively voluminous that it can be grasped in the hand and brought forward well away from the teeth so as to fill the palm of the hand as a rubber ball might do. The fact is made use of by many horsemen who place a cord or wooden 'twitch' tightly on the upper lip as a means of restraint during various procedures disapproved of by the horse.

The lower lip is applied more tightly to the incisor teeth than the upper lip with less slack to spare. It carries beneath it a some-what rounded mass the *prominence of the chin*. This is formed by an admixture of fibrous tissue, fat and the levator muscle which raises the lower lip. The lower lip however, moves but little, whereas the upper lip can be projected and used in the manner of a miniature trunk to muzzle the ground or the floor of a manger in search of grain or even grass.

The *cheeks* form the sides of the mouth and are continuous in front with the lips. The internal lining layer of both lips and cheeks is reflected above and below onto the *gums*, and is reddish in colour frequently showing pigmented areas.

The *tongue* may be inspected by parting the lips and inserting the hand in the interspace between the incisor and cheek teeth. The front end of the tongue is free and spatulate in shape and can be drawn out of the mouth and examined. The hind end or *root* is thick and cannot be moved from its resting position. It is three sided and it fills the space between the two halves of the lower jaw in the floor of the mouth. It is a highly muscular organ, in fact practically solid muscle throughout. These muscles move the tongue in a variety of directions and some originate from outside the body of the tongue from the hyoid bone and the ramus of the mandible (Fig. 34).

When the *tip of the tongue* is drawn out and raised it will be seen that its movement is somewhat limited as it is attached to the floor of the mouth by a fold of mucous membrane known as the *frenulum linguae*. On either side of the frenulum in the mucous membrane of the floor of the mouth are a pair of raised papillae which indicate the position of the openings of the *submandibular salivary glands*.

The mucous membrane covering the tongue surface is raised into *papillae* of four kinds:

(a) *filiform papillae*, closely packed fine, greyish structures giving a pile to the upper surface (dorsum);

(b) *fungiform papillae*, flattened, mushroom shaped, scattered along dorsum and sides;

(c) *circumvalate papillae*, one on each side of the dorsal midline 5 inches from the laryngeal opening, each is surrounded by a trench;

(d) *foliate papillae*, on the dorsum and sides just in front of the anterior pillars of the soft palate.

The papillae are the seat of nerve endings mediating the sense of taste.

The roof of the mouth is formed from the *hard palate* in front and the *soft palate* close behind and continuous with it (Fig. 34). The hard palate is covered by a dense mucous membrane divided centrally and longitudinally by a median raphe which is crossed by about eighteen or twenty curved ridges, their convex edges pointing forwards. It is partly concave and bounded behind, on either side, by the *premolar* and *molar teeth*. At the front the hard palate fills the interspace between the two sides of the jaw. In stallions and geldings over $3\frac{1}{2}$–4 years old there will be a *canine tooth* or *tush* in this space, one on either side of the mouth. In mares this tush is usually absent or else quite rudimentary. The hard palate extends in a forward direction as far as the concavity provided at the rear of the upper *incisor teeth* (Fig. 2).

The soft palate is an oblique, valve-like, musculomembranous curtain separating the mouth cavity from the *pharynx*. Its anterior (oral) surface looks downwards and forwards and is covered with mucous membrane continuous with that of the hard palate. On each side a short fold passes down to the sides of the tongue, the *anterior pillars of the soft palate*. Owing to the length of the soft palate in the horse, the free border contacting the *epiglottis* of the *larynx*, the *common pharynx* may be regarded as being closed off from the oral cavity except during the passage of food or drink towards the *oesophagus* (Fig. 34). The free border is continued on either side by a membranous fold in the pharyngeal wall, the *posterior pillar of the soft palate*. The pharyngeal wall between the two pillars of the palate is occupied by the *diffuse tonsil*. The large size of the soft palate explains why the horse has difficulty mouth breathing. Also it is one of the reasons why a horse has difficulty vomitting. If vomitting does occur the ejected matter escapes usually through the nose.

By withdrawing the front portion of the tongue between the lips, making use of the *interdental space*, and raising the head, one can inspect the premolar and molar teeth of one side at a time using the tongue drawn across the interdental space as a gag. Notice the disposition of the premolars and molars. At birth the foal has three cheek teeth; at 2 years old, five; at 4 to 5 years old it has a complete set of six cheek teeth. Notice sharp edges, uneven wear, a step mouth in which some teeth project farther than others, missing teeth, caries, or teeth worn down nearly to the gums.

THE FACIAL MUSCLES

The *cutaneous muscle* is not continuous beneath the skin of the face except for a few disconnected bundles, but a supplementary sheet

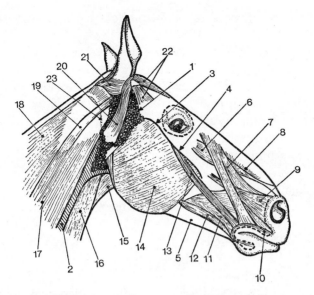

FIG. 35. Muscles of the head in lateral view. (After Ellenberger, Baum and Dittrich.)
(1) Parotid gland. (2) Jugular vein. (3) Zygomatic arch. (4) Facial crest. (5)
Ramus of mandible. (6) Levator muscle of the upper lip. (7) Levator nasolabialis
muscle. (8) Dorsal part of lateral nasal muscle. (9) Lateral nostril dilator muscle.
(10) Orbicularis oris muscle. (11) Buccinator muscle. (12) Depressor muscle of the
lower lip. (13) Zygomaticus muscle. (14) Masseter muscle. (15) Omohyoid muscle.
(16) Sternocephalic muscle. (17) Brachiocephalic muscle. (18) Splenius muscle.
(19) Mastoid tendon of the brachiocephalic muscle. (20) Parotido-auricular muscle.
(21) Cervico-auricular muscle. (22) Scutularis muscle. (23) Wing of atlas.

elaborates as a superficial layer of *facial muscles* (Fig. 35). The two
components can produce wrinkling of the overlying skin giving
expression to the face. The facial muscles are concentrated around
the orifices, the mouth, nostrils and eyes, and generally originate
from the bones of the muzzle (frontal, nasal, maxilla, etc.).

The mouth and the eye have sphincter (closing) muscles
around them, the *orbicularis oris* in the lips, and the *orbicularis
oculi* in the eyelids. Both also have dilator (opening) muscles. Thus
below the eye between the facial crest and the outer edges of the
nasal bone, you may observe a slight longitudinal ridge produced
by the *levator* or *lifting muscles of the upper lip*. Part of this muscle
also acts as a *nostril dilator*, raising the outer wing of the nostril.
The levator muscles of the upper lip can raise it so that a horse
exhibits all its incisor teeth with the lip completely everted. Sometimes the horse does this when it smells a titbit of food, while at

other times it appears to perform the trick merely to attract attention.

The skin over the space between the nasal peak and upper jaw (the *nasomaxillary notch*) is free and very flexible and is associated with three separate *dilator muscles* on either side (Fig. 35). These dilators are attached to the cartilages in the nostril wings so that raising of the skin covering the nasal passage and dilatation of the nostril of the same side are synchronized.

The lower lip is provided with a *depressor muscle*, and the cheeks contain a large muscular sheet, the *buccinator muscle*, which can flatten them thus pressing food between the teeth.

Finally the external ear has a set of superficial muscles associated with the three cartilages, arising from the surface of the head and neck. These muscles can 'prick up' the ears so that the opening is directed forwards, or 'lay back' the ears so that the opening faces backwards.

The importance of all these superficial muscles, especially those of the eyelids and lips, can be appreciated when a horse suffering from paralysis of these muscles is examined.

THE INTERMANDIBULAR SPACE

This space lies below and between the two halves of the lower jawbone, the *mandibular rami*. These are largely subcutaneous back to the angle of the jaw and are crossed by the *facial artery* and *vein* and the *duct of the parotid salivary gland* midway between the body and the angle of the jaw. The lower edge of the mandible is thus an admirable place to feel the horse's pulse. Run the tip of the finger along the inner edge of the bone and, by maintaining gentle pressure on the outer surface of the jaw with the thumb, the gentle throb of the pulse may be felt with the fingertip quite easily as the artery crosses the jaw 3 inches from the angle. The normal pulse rate is 35 beats per minute in the resting horse with a variation between 28 and 40. The pulse rate increases very rapidly with fast exercise.

In the centre of the intermandibular space, immediately below the skin, lie the *mandibular lymph glands* arranged in two elongated groups in a V-shape. These are the glands which become swollen and inflamed in influenza and throat infections, and are often the seat of abscesses in strangles.

In the middle of the hindermost part of the intermandibular space the *larynx* is palpable, joined up with the *trachea* as the latter passes down the neck (Figs. 32 and 34). Gently squeezing the trachea, especially near the larynx, will make a horse cough, and the sound of the cough so induced may be used by veterinary surgeons in their diagnoses. The sound may be the key to any type of respiratory trouble existent. The larynx is a short tubular structure at the opening of pharynx into trachea, the passage leading from the nasal chamber to the lung. It is made up of five cartilages articulated together. These serve as attachment areas for muscles which open and close the *glottis* (the opening into the larynx) by tightening or slackening the mucous membrane. The single, median *epiglottis* is the most anterior of the cartilages and projects up in front of the glottis (Fig. 34). Whenever the horse swallows and food passes from the mouth it must cross the opening of the larynx, which lies in the floor of the pharynx, to gain entrance to the oesophagus, the food passage to the stomach. The glottic closure muscles contract and the epiglottis is bent backwards over the aperture of the larynx by being pressed against the base of the tongue. The glottis is thus sealed off when food passes over it. Paralysis of the muscles activating one of the two *arytenoid cartilages*, usually that of the left side, causes partial obstruction of the glottis by the mucous membrane covering the vocal fold becoming flaccid. This is the condition known as 'roaring'.

The larynx is suspended from the base of the skull by the *hyoid apparatus* (Fig. 6). The *thyroid cornua* of the hyoid articulate with the *thyroid cartilage* of the larynx, and a membrane passes between them on either side. The hyoid bone is placed at the root of the tongue and much of the tongue musculature has its origin on the hyoid apparatus (Fig. 34). Also a special projection, the *lingual process*, extends forwards from the hyoid into the body of the tongue. In this way the hyoid supports the tongue and enables it to move about in the floor of the mouth.

THE NECK AND POLL

Let us now study the horse's poll and neck as far down as the shoulders. Immediately behind the jawbone, and following its vertical margin, is a furrow which commences at the base of the ear and extends down to the angle of the jaw (Fig. 32). This groove widens out to become continuous with the *jugular furrow* which passes down the length of the neck.

The *parotid gland* is the largest of the salivary glands and one which can easily be felt with the fingers as it lies almost directly beneath the skin. The gland commences at the root of the ear (*conchal cartilage*) and stretches downwards filling up the space between the wing of the atlas (which is subcutaneous) and the edge of the lower jaw (Fig. 35). Between the skin and the outer surface of the gland is a thin layer of muscular tissue. The upper end of the parotid gland embraces the root of the ear, while its lower end is bordered by the *external maxillary vein*. Below and behind the base of the ear the parotid gland abuts onto the *brachiocephalic muscle*. The *internal maxillary vein* passes through the substance of the parotid gland to join with the external maxillary to form the *jugular vein* at the lower and hinder corner of the gland.

The *wing of the atlas* lies at the extreme upper part of the neck behind the base of the ear. Its prominent rim is subcutaneous and lies a few inches below the level of the mane. In front it bounds the parotid gland while behind it a shallow furrow runs obliquely down the neck. This represents the upper border of the brachio-cephalic muscle (Chart Three). This muscle is present in the neck and arm and has an important bearing on forelimb action. It is a long, flattened, rather fleshy muscle arising from the mastoid process of the temporal bone behind the ear, and also from the wing of the atlas and the transverse processes of the second, third and fourth cervical vertebrae. After travelling down the whole length of the neck it is inserted into the *deltoid tuberosity and crest of the humerus* and the fascia of the shoulder and arm. When the muscle contracts it pulls the arm forwards but its efficiency depends to some extent upon the position of the head at the time. This explains why a horse moves more freely in front when the head is either fully extended upon the neck or carried high. It also indicates the disadvantage of riding on a tight rein and of harnessing the head and neck into unnatural positions, especially by use of fixed martingales. In the neck the brachiocephalic muscle can be seen beneath the skin and can be palpated over a considerable part of its course. Its degree of development should be noted when judging a horse for fitness and is just as important as that of the forearm or second thigh.

In its passage down the neck the brachiocephalic muscle forms the upper boundary of the jugular groove. It passes over the front of the shoulder joint and inserts onto the shaft of the humerus. It is a powerful muscle having a two way action. When the head is advanced and the neck held firmly by its own muscles, contraction of the brachiocephalic carries the arm and knee forwards to the maximum degree attainable. When the horse is standing still contraction of either muscle will help to turn the head to the same side.

The *sternocephalic muscle* is another long and narrow muscle which extends from the *sternum* to the *angle of the jaw* (Fig. 35). It forms the ventral boundary of the jugular furrow. In the groove the jugular vein is subcutaneous and parallel with it, but deeper in, runs the *common carotid artery*. Down the lower margin of the neck through the thin strap-like *sternothyrohyoid muscles* the *trachea* or windpipe is easily felt. On the left side of the neck the *oesophagus* lies along the upper surface of the trachea in the same plane as the jugular vein. Although the oesophagus is not readily discernible it becomes so when the horse eats or drinks and the material swallowed dilates it as it descends.

In the lighter breeds in particular, the *transverse processes of the cervical vertebrae* are deeply palpable on the lateral surface of the neck (Fig. 32). These processes are most apparent half-way down the neck, and lie relatively low in the neck at this point. Farther up the neck they assume a higher level but their firm substance can still be felt by the fingers.

THE FORELIMB

THE SHOULDER

The important concept to grasp in the consideration of the shoulder is the importance of many muscles in this region in helping to tie the limb to the body, there being no bony union (Fig. 43 in the Appendix). The muscles act as weight supporters and shock absorbers since practically two thirds of the body weight are carried on the thoracic limbs. The chief landmarks in the shoulder region are:

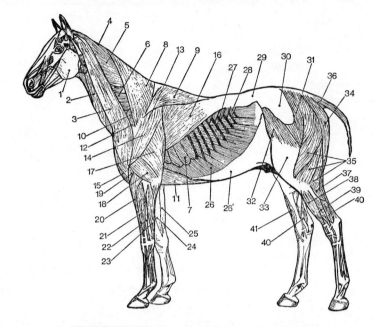

CHART THREE. The superficial muscles of the horse.

(1) Masseter. (2) Sternocephalic. (3) Brachiocephalic. (4) Rhomboideus. (5) Splenius. (6) Cervical part of serratus ventralis. (7) Thoracic part of serratus ventralis. (8) Cervical part of trapezius. (9) Thoracic part of trapezius. (10) Anterior deep pectoral. (11) Posterior deep pectoral. (12) Supraspinatus. (13) Infraspinatus. (14) Deltoid. (15) Anterior superficial pectoral. (16) Latissimus dorsi. (17) Long head of triceps. (18) Lateral head of triceps. (19) Brachialis. (20) Extensor carpi radialis. (21) Common digital extensor. (22) Lateral digital extensor. (23) Ulnaris lateralis. (24) Flexor carpi radialis. (25) Flexor carpi ulnaris. (26) External abdominal oblique. (26′) Aponeurosis of external abdominal oblique. (27) External intercostal. (28) Serratus dorsalis caudalis. (29) Lumbo-dorsal fascia. (30) Gluteal fascia. (31) Superficial gluteal. (32) Tensor fasciae latae. (33) Fascia lata. (34) Semitendinosus. (35) Biceps femoris. (36) Sacrococcygeals. (37) Lateral head of gastrocnemius. (38) Long digital extensor. (39) Lateral digital extensor. (40) Deep digital flexor. (41) Tibialis anterior.

(a) the upward rise of the shoulder away from its junction with the neck;
(b) the withers;
(c) the spine of the scapula;
(d) the point of the shoulder;
(e) the sternum and pectoral muscles;
(f) the triceps muscle mass.

In a well-rounded *shoulder* the junction between neck and shoulder is gradual and streamlined, except perhaps in harness horses in which some seating for the collar is sometimes favourable. In most cases however, a collar fits a streamlined shoulder quite well providing the shoulder has sufficient width on either side to accommodate it.

The *withers* constitute the highest point of the thoracic spine and are formed by the *dorsal spinous processes* of the third to the tenth thoracic vertebrae. The highest point of all is created by the fourth and fifth spinous processes (Chart One). The withers are held firmly in place by ligaments between them, and by a series of ligaments and muscles which are attached to the spines. These include the *funicular portion of the nuchal ligament* (Fig. 8). The dorsal spinous processes also give anchorage to a number of muscles which greatly relieve the sharpness of the withers and help to mould the region into the general contour without creating an unpleasant sharpness of the spinal ridge (Chart Two). Firstly a flattened triangular sheet of superficial muscle, the *trapezius*. This originates by its base from the midline of the neck, withers and thorax, i.e., the funicular part of the nuchal ligament and the *supraspinous ligament* back to the tenth thoracic vertebra (Chart Three). The apex of the triangular sheet is inserted into the scapular spine. Deep to the trapezius is the *rhomboideus muscle* which ties the scapula into the sides of the spinous processes and the ligamentum nuchae (Figs. 36 and 43). This muscle, like the trapezius, has both thoracic and cervical parts.

The division between neck and shoulder is marked by the presence of the scapula with its two overlying muscles on either side of the scapular spine. This spine is plainly visible beneath the skin in anything but an overfat horse. The muscles are the *supraspinatus* in front and the *infraspinatus* behind the spine (Fig. 36). Both muscles insert onto the lateral tuberosity of the upper end

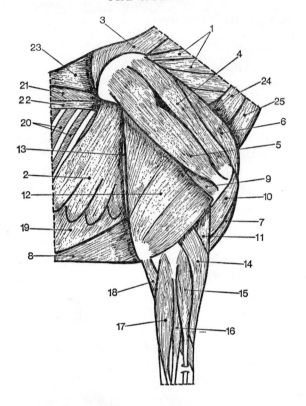

FIG. 36. Deep muscles of the shoulder and arm in lateral view.
(1) Cervical part of serratus ventralis. (2) Thoracic part of serratus ventralis. (3) Rhomboideus. (4) Supraspinatus. (5) Infraspinatus. (6) Anterior deep pectoral. (7) Anterior superficial pectoral. (8) Posterior deep pectoral. (9) Teres minor. (10) Biceps brachii. (11) Brachialis. (12) Triceps long head. (13) Tensor fasciae antebrachii. (14) Extensor carpi radialis. (15) Common digital extensor. (16) Lateral digital extensor. (17) Ulnaris lateralis. (18) Deep digital flexor (ulnar head). (19) External abdominal oblique. (20) External intercostals. (21) Longissimus dorsi. (22) Longissimus costarum. (23) Spinalis dorsi. (24) Omohyoid. (25) Sternocephalic.

of the humerus close to the shoulder joint. Because of the exposed position of the joint both muscles have synovial bursae beneath their tendons of insertion. The muscles when well developed raise the level of the skin overlying the scapula. Excessive development of these muscles, more commonly in a horse in which the scapula is upright rather than oblique, is frowned upon since it is considered that they cramp the shoulder action.

The scapular spine and the fascia covering the infraspinatus muscle also give origin to the *deltoideus muscle* which can be felt on the outside of the shoulder joint as it passes down onto the deltoid tuberosity of the humerus (Chart Three). The deltoid contacts the *brachiocephalic* in front which also has an insertion onto the deltoid tuberosity after crossing, and being moulded on, the front of the shoulder.

It is important when examining the outer aspect of the shoulder to observe the degree of scapular obliquity. In other words to take note of whether the shoulder slopes backward between its two extremities, or whether it lies vertically. This degree of inclination can be accurately noted by the practised eye, but the novice may gain a better idea by drawing a chalk line from the point of the shoulder to the upper end of the scapular spine, then another from the point of the shoulder parallel with the ground, and measuring the angle formed between the two lines. By carrying out the same procedure on a number of horses and then comparing their visible conformation with the angles of inclination obtained, one will quickly learn to assess the degree of inclination by the eye alone.

It is preferable that the scapula should incline well backward at its upper end enabling the horse to advance the limb and carry the knee and foot as far forward as possible. It should be noted that however good the action may be, very few horses at the walk bring the front of the knee farther forward than a line dropped vertically from the point of the shoulder. When trotting the knee may advance to a line dropped from the poll. During a gallop the toes of the forefeet may reach as far as a line dropped from the nose when the head is moderately extended. Even at the height of the gallop with head outstretched the foot seldom advances to the level of a line dropped at this moment from the horse's nose.

Endurance seems to be adversely affected by an upright shoulder, and although many horses thus furnished attain a respectable speed they have to perform a good deal more work in order to attain it. Incidentally, a horse with an upright shoulder is unable to substantially reduce the concussion arising from hammering the hoofs upon the ground. If I may mention it, quite a lot of the same concussive force is transferred to the rider's posterior and up his or her spine.

If we look for a moment at the shoulder from in front we can identify the *cariniform cartilage* at the front end of the sternum. This lies in the middle line of the chest at the base of the neck. From the sternum the *pectoral muscles* pass downwards and outwards to converge on the humerus in the region of the crest of the greater tuberosity. The pectorals also insert onto the lesser tuberosity and into the fascia of the arm and forearm (Fig. 43 in the Appendix). The pectoral muscles therefore form a triangular sheet with the base on the sternum and the apex on the humerus. Of the pectoral muscle complex the *superficial pectorals* form a distinct prominence on the front of the chest easily recognizable in the living animal. The *deep pectoral muscle* is represented here by an anterior portion which takes its origin from the lateral surface of the anterior part of the sternum. It passes forwards and upwards over the front of the shoulder beneath the brachiocephalic muscle towards the cranial angle of the scapula on the supraspinatus muscle (Fig. 36 and Chart Three). It attaches to the fascia covering the supraspinatus muscle and onto the scapula directly at the cranial angle. The importance of this division of the pectoral muscles will become evident later in Part Three.

The front border of the pectoral muscles meets the lower border of the brachiocephalic muscle over much of the front of the shoulder, but they separate at the *supraclavicular fossa* beside the *manubrium of the sternum*. This fossa is clearly palpable and is located at the lower end of the jugular groove noticed earlier.

At all times the *point of the shoulder* can be seen and felt. This point is formed from the greater tuberosity of the upper end of the humerus which stands out in front of the joint surface. The *biceps brachii muscle* passes across the front of the shoulder joint in the intertuberal groove of the humerus from an origin on the scapular tuberosity. It travels downwards to its insertion into the radial tuberosity on the inner side of the head of the radius. This muscle flexes the elbow joint and extends the shoulder. It can be located as it passes down the upper arm overlying the front of the humerus (Fig. 36). Where the tendon passes over the intertuberal groove it is lubricated by a synovial bursa. This occupies the most anterior and prominent site in the forelimb and is exposed to injury from bruising. This is a common cause of shoulder lameness, although shoulder lameness, despite common belief, is not a very frequent cause of lameness in the horse.

The *triceps muscle* mass comprises three separate muscles extending between the hinder edge of the scapula and the olecranon process or *point of the elbow* (Fig. 36). They produce the plump rounded mass of muscle lying alongside the ribs just above the elbow joint. This is the triangular portion which bulges just in front of the flap of the saddle and rests against the rider's knee or shin. The *long head of the triceps* is the largest part of the muscle and originates on the scapula, it therefore has a flexing action on the shoulder as well as an extending action on the elbow joint. The two remaining heads of the triceps, the *lateral head* and *medial head*, are both shorter and have their origins on the hinder side of the humeral shaft. These two heads only cross the elbow joint and so will have the sole action of elbow extension.

An important muscle in the make-up of the horse is the *latissimus dorsi* which lies behind the shoulder region covering the side of the chest and extending up onto the back (Chart Three). From its broad origin from the midline of the back in the thoracic and lumbar regions the muscle fibres converge to end on the teres tuberosity of the humerus in common with the *teres major muscle*. This latter muscle lies deeply against the posterior surface of the scapula and is one of the major flexors of the shoulder joint. The latissimus dorsi also finds extensive insertion onto the fascia in the upper arm.

THE FOREARM AND KNEE

Both the *forearm* and the *second thigh* require close consideration since these act as the media between body and earth and need be strongly developed to stand up to the amount of work and strain demanded of them. At the elbow the *olecranon process* of the ulna (the point of the elbow) is distinctly visible (Fig. 15), and both *lateral epicondyle of the humerus* and *lateral tuberosity of the radius* are palpable. The radius and ulna are hidden by muscles except at the lower part of the inner surface of the forearm above the knee where the radius lies beneath the skin.

The muscle mass in front of the limb from the elbow down has its origin mainly on the lateral epicondyle of the humerus and the lateral tuberosity of the radius. Contained in this muscle mass are

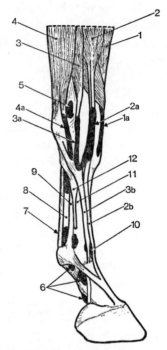

FIG. 37. Muscles, tendons and tendon sheaths of the lower part of the forelimb in
lateral view. (After Bradley.)
(1, 1a) Extensor carpi radialis and synovial sheath. (2, 2a, 2b) Common digital
extensor muscle, synovial sheath and tendon. (3, 3a, 3b) Lateral digital extensor
muscle, synovial sheath and tendon. (4, 4a) Ulnaris lateralis muscle and synovial
sheath of its long tendon. (5) Carpal synovial sheath. (6) Digital synovial sheath.
(7) Superficial digital flexor tendon. (8) Deep digital flexor tendon. (9) Suspensory
ligament. (10) Synovial bursa under extensor tendons. (11) Large metacarpal bone.
(12) Small metacarpal bone.

the extensor muscles of both knee and digit which carry the limb
and foot forward. The most important are the *extensor carpi radialis*
acting on the knee and the *common digital extensor* acting on both
knee and digit (Fig. 36). The carpal bones are only evident as a
group, but over the front of the knee the extensor tendons pass in
canals formed by thickened fascia and connective tissue each
tendon protected by its own enveloping synovial sheath (Fig. 37).
These tendons can be felt with the finger-tips, and their synovial
sheaths often become involved in cases of 'broken knees' arising
from falls.

The muscle mass at the back of the limb from the elbow has its origin mainly on the large medial epicondyle of the humerus and the olecranon process. Contained in it are the flexor muscles of the carpus, fetlock and digit. Included are both *superficial* and *deep digital flexors* as well as the *carpal flexor muscles*. At the outer side and back of the knee the *accessory carpal bone* can be seen and felt protruding behind the limb. A ridge on its upper surface corresponding with the insertion into it of the tendons of the *ulnaris lateralis* and *flexor carpi ulnaris*, the knee flexors. The concave inner surface of the accessory carpal bone helps to form the carpal canal. The tendons of the digital flexor muscles travel down through the carpal canal at the back of the knee. The knee requires little more description, as it has been discussed in Part One (Figs. 16 and 17). You may feel the rows of bones especially if the foot is lifted a little from the ground when the rows of bones become slightly separated.

Returning to the region of the elbow the lower tendon of the biceps brachii muscle inserts into the radial tuberosity on the inner side of the head of the radius. This upper end of the radius is covered lightly by the *superficial pectoral muscle* which is thin enough here to allow the tuberosity to be palpated through it. Just behind the biceps tendon the *median nerve* and the comparatively large *median artery* may be felt as they lie on the radius. Both artery and nerve can be felt by rolling them beneath the fingertip against the radial tuberosity. This makes a very convenient site at which to take the pulse, in addition to the facial artery beneath the lower jaw which we have seen.

On the inner side of the forearm, at its lower third, the 'chestnut' is located. This is a horny oval callosity of uncertain origin and uncertain function.

THE METACARPUS AND DIGIT

From the knee down is a very important part of every hunter, racehorse and steeplechaser. Within its compass all the tendons and ligaments which are made use of to support the weight of the body and move it from place to place are found.

The *metacarpal bones*, one large and two small, are mainly subcutaneous and they can be palpated very easily. The lower extremities of the splint bones are unmistakable small nodular prominences. Any acquired bony adhesions or exostoses existing between the large and small metacarpals can be felt with the fingers. The metacarpal tuberosity at the front of the cannon bone, below the knee, can be felt, onto which the *extensor carpi radialis* (knee extensor) attaches. Below this the *common digital extensor tendon* runs down the front of the cannon and phalanges to pass onto the extensor process of the third phalanx within the hoof.

Behind the fetlock the proximal sesamoid bones can be felt, but as they are tightly encased in ligaments and covered by flexor tendons their detail is not easy to determine (Figs. 18, 19 and 21). The position of these sesamoids is indicated by a tuft of hairs surmounting a horny callosity, the *ergot*, equivalent to the meta-carpal pad of the dog. However, immediately above the proximal sesamoid bones at the hinderpart of the outer surface of the fetlock, the fingertips can be inserted in the small space between the hind tendons and the metacarpal bone. At the bottom of this space one can feel the *digital artery* pulsating and also the *volar nerve* and *common digital vein* can be rolled beneath the finger-tips. The artery divides into medial and lateral branches which can be felt as they pass out from the space over the sides of the fetlock.

The tendons of the superficial and deep digital flexor muscles are outstanding features of the foot. The *superficial flexor tendon* begins above the carpus and is joined by a strong fibrous band, the *radial* or *superior check ligament* which fuses with the tendon near to the carpus. The tendon continues down through the *carpal canal* in the *carpal synovial sheath* (Fig. 19). In the cannon region the tendon flattens and widens into a ring above the fetlock through which the tendon of the *deep flexor muscle* passes. The superficial flexor tendon divides into two parts below the fetlock, attached on either side of the hinder part of the first and second phalanges. Through the fork thus created the deep flexor tendon passes on its way, within the *digital synovial sheath*, to be inserted into the sole of the third phalanx at the semilunar crest (Fig. 37). A bursa is interposed at this point, the *navicular bursa*, between the deep flexor tendon and the distal sesamoid bone (Fig. 19).

The two flexor tendons, one overlying the other, can be felt easily, but unless the horse is young or has done little work it is not always easy to separate them by touch. Tendons such as these are apt to become more and more united by fibrous tissue as the years go on. These 'back tendons' are not the only structures existing behind the metacarpal bone between it and the skin, as many horsemen know to their cost. The deep digital flexor tendon is united to the back of the knee by a 4 inch fibrous band, the *subcarpal* or *inferior check ligament*. When excessive strain falls on the deep flexor this ligament takes part of the weight and often becomes thickened and strained.

Between the deep flexor tendon and the cannon bone there is a flat, elastic band about an inch wide which takes origin from the back of the knee, then passes down the limb. At the lower third of the cannon bone it bifurcates to make two branches, one of which is inserted into the upper part of each sesamoid bone (Fig. 21). This ligamentous band is known as the *suspensory ligament* and occupies the channel present between the back of the metacarpal bone and the small splint bones. Like the other structures behind the cannon this ligament is also subject to strain. Below the proximal sesamoid bones it sends two tendinous cords to travel in a forward direction to be inserted, one on either side, into the common extensor tendon at the front of the limb (Fig. 21).

It is easier to distinguish these various structures by touch if the foot is lifted and the fetlock, pastern and coffin joints are slightly flexed. In any instance in which lameness arises it is better to leave the diagnosis of the affected part to a veterinary surgeon since each separate structure may require special treatment. In many cases more than one of the structures may be involved. Inflammation of tendons gives rise to swelling, heat and pain. Ultimately repair of the strained and torn tendon fibres is accomplished by the laying down of new fibrous tissue. This has a habit of contracting after union has been effected, with the result that the tendons also contract (become shortened). The consequence is that some degree of fetlock flexion occurs as a permanent feature. The fetlock and foot may then assume different positions in relation to the rest of the limb and to one another.

THE TRUNK

The *trunk* consists basically of *thorax* and *abdomen* slung between the forelimbs in a muscular cradle in front, and rigidly attached by a bony union with the hindlimbs at the rear. Its surface indicates a number of important features and a number of important areas. For our purposes we will divide it into three divisions, the upper surface of the *back* and *loins*, the *chest* and the *abdomen* (Chart Two).

The *back*, *loins* and *croup* form the upper contour of the body from the withers back to the sacrum. It has as its bony basis the last eleven or twelve thoracic vertebrae together with the upper extremities of the corresponding ribs, the lumbar vertebrae, the front part of the sacrum and the pelvis from croup to haunches. The contour, however, is moulded around the muscles lying above the vertebral column, between the spinous processes dorsally and the transverse processes laterally. These muscles are arranged in a longitudinal series extending forwards from the region of the croup and haunches. These attach en route to the spinous processes and transverse processes and the upper ends of the ribs. The *longissimus dorsi* is the major component and is the largest and longest muscle in the body. Posteriorly it is greatly developed to form the common mass of the loins above the lumbar vertebrae. Further forwards it fills in the space between the spinous processes and ribs, the costovertebral groove of the back. These muscles are broadly palpable underneath a strong tendinous sheet, the *lumbodorsal fascia*, in the loins and hind part of the back. Towards the withers the latissimus dorsi and trapezius muscles cover the epaxial longissimus system (Chart Three and Fig. 36).

The *back* is of primary importance because it receives the saddle and the weight of the rider as well as transmitting to the front part of the body the efforts of propulsion, which are communicated through the loins by the hindlimbs.

The *chest* corresponds to the bony thoracic rib-cage, bounded above by the withers and back, in front by the neck, on each side by the shoulder, arm and ribs, below by the sternum and behind by the abdomen. Only the hinder parts are available for examination (behind the shoulder and arm) but much of this is covered by muscle. Thus both *latissimus dorsi* and *pectoral muscles* cover the ribs (Chart Three), and the *cutaneous muscle* of the skin is quite thick behind the arm. These all tend to obscure from view an important weight supporting muscle, the *serratus ventralis*. However, its serrated lower border attaching to the ribs may be felt on the chest wall (Chart Three and Fig. 36). Further back the limit of the rib-cage, the *costal arch*, may be felt as it arches downwards and forwards from the beginning of the lumbar region to the *xiphoid of the sternum* (Chart One). Even this has a superficial covering of muscles, the *abdominal wall muscles* which spread forwards to have part of their origins on the surface of the rib-cage. The ribs may be clearly felt in the upper hinder portion of the chest where they will be found to be clearly separated by intercostal spaces filled with *intercostal musculature*.

The chest can be seen to accomplish regular, alternative movements, which are more or less extensive according to the state of respiration. These respiratory movements are especially perceptible in thinner (emaciated) horses, and are of two basic kinds:

(1) *inspiratory*, in which the intercostal spaces are augmented and the ribs are rotated forwards and outwards resulting in a dilatation of the thoracic cavity and an enlargement of the lungs and therefore an inflow of air;

(2) *expiratory*, in which the ribs are approximated and rotated backwards and inwards, contracting the thorax and compressing the lungs, driving air out.

The intercostal muscles are responsible for only a part of the respiratory movements, other deeper muscles are involved, in particular the muscular partition between the thoracic and abdominal cavities, the *diaphragm*.

The abdomen lies behind the costal arch, below the loins, and in front of the haunch, thigh and stifle. It is normally spoken of in terms of *flanks* and *belly* (Chart Two). The abdominal wall is formed from several layers of muscle, the *external abdominal oblique, internal abdominal oblique* and *transverse abdominal*. These muscular layers are important since they support the weight of the viscera. When examining the chest we noticed that these abdominal muscles have rib attachments. They also find attachments from the dense tendinous sheet covering the loins, and from the haunch bones, the ilia and the pubic areas of the pelvic bones. Weight pressing down on the inside of the abdominal wall is distributed upwards, forwards and backwards by these lateral abdominal muscles together with the *rectus abdominis muscle* in the midline of the belly. The surface features you can identify are relatively few, there is a hollow in the flank just in front of the haunch, and the lower part of the flank is united to the stifle by a very mobile fold of skin. This skin fold contains part of the *cutaneous muscle* of the skin which finds attachment to the patella. The lower silhouette of the belly should show a graceful curve up and back from the sternum to the groin on the inner side of the thigh.

The whole abdominal wall is elastic and yields to pressure from a fingertip. As it is composed of soft structures attached to the ribs, and the diaphragm forms the front margin of the cavity, the abdomen mirrors the movements of the chest in respiration.

THE HINDLIMB

THE HIP, THIGH AND BUTTOCK

The *thigh* is the region where the hindlimb becomes separated from the trunk. It is limited above by the haunch, croup and quarters, below by the leg and stifle, in front by the flank, and it is free behind (Chart Two). The anatomical bases of this region are the pelvic bone, the femur and the associated muscles. The chief landmarks which affect the shape of the horse in the hip and thigh region when viewed from the outside are:

(a) the *tuber coxae*, 'point of the haunch' or 'pin bone' (the two pin bones may be viewed simultaneously from behind the horse, occasionally one becomes 'knocked down' and is accordingly lower than the other);

(b) the *tuber sacrale*, 'point of the croup', the highest point at the rear of the horse;

(c) the *major trochanter of the femur*, 'point of the hip', although deep can be felt from the surface;

(d) the *tuber ischii*, 'point of the buttock' or 'seat bone', one on either side of and a few inches below the tail;

(e) the *third trochanter of the femur* in the upper part of the thigh;

(f) the *lateral epicondyle of the femur* and the patella at the stifle.

The hindquarters extend out, back and down from the point of the croup, consisting of a mass of muscle which clothes the buttock and the outer and rear surface of hip and thigh down to the stifle and leg. Immediately behind the croup and arising from the shaft of the ilium (and from both tuber sacrale and tuber coxae, and the sacroiliac and sacrosciatic ligaments) is the bulk

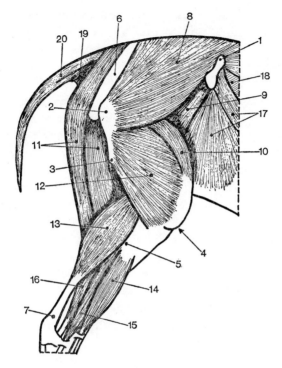

FIG. 38. Deep muscles of the hip, thigh and leg in lateral view.
(1) Tuber coxae. (2) Major trochanter of femur. (3) Third trochanter of femur.
(4) Patella. (5) Lateral tibial condyle. (6) Sacrosciatic ligament. (7) Achilles
tendon. (8) Medial gluteal. (9) Iliopsoas. (10) Rectus femoris. (11) Semitendinosus. (12) Vastus lateralis. (13) Gastrocnemius. (14) Long digital extensor. (15)
Lateral digital extensor. (16) Deep digital flexor. (17) Internal abdominal oblique.
(18) Transverse abdominal. (19) Coccygeal. (20) Sacrococcygeals.

of the muscle mass which gives the haunch its rounded contour,
the *gluteal muscles* (Chart Three and Fig. 38). These muscles have
insertions on the major and third trochanters and the femoral
shaft between the two. In front of this group is a dense superficial
tendinous layer containing a muscle which is indistinguishable on
palpation from the gluteal mass. It is the *tensor fasciae latae* and
originates on the tuber coxae (Chart Three). The tendinous fascia
associated with it clothes the front part of the thigh and attaches
to the *patella* and thus onto the *tibial crest* of the second thigh.
The hindpart of the quarters is formed from a rounded muscle
mass extending from the sacral and coccygeal vertebrae down the
outer and hind side of the thigh to attach to the outer surface of

the stifle joint. It also has attachments to both inner and outer surfaces of the tibia, and to the tuber calcis through the dense fascia of the lower leg. This muscle mass is very important and needs to be considered more closely. The *biceps femoris muscle* is large and related to the hind edge of the gluteal mass, in fact a slight groove may be felt between them (Chart Three). It passes in a curved direction down the thigh covering the greater trochanter, to the lateral surface of the leg where it is readily felt from the surface. The attachment areas of this muscle are complex, so are its actions as we shall see later in Part Three. Broadly speaking three parts of the muscle are represented each having a different area of insertion. The most anterior part attaches to the rear surface of the femur near the third trochanter, as well as to the patella and lateral patellar ligament (Fig. 27). The second part attaches to the crest of the tibia below the stifle joint. The third part attaches to the dense fascia (crural fascia) which encases the lower part of the leg and attaches to the tuber calcis, the point of the hock. This part assists in the formation of the posterior contour of the limb and is associated with the *tarsal tendon*.

The *semitendinosus muscle* is long and extends along the hind border of the biceps femoris down the back of the thigh having passed over the seat bone (tuber ischii) en route. Thus it is distinctly palpable for much of its length (Chart Three). The muscle terminates on a wide tendon on the inner surface of the stifle joint. This tendon has attachments onto the tibial crest and the fascia of the leg, and has a part which joins with the tarsal tendon of the biceps femoris to terminate on the tuber calcis of the hock.

The *semimembranosus muscle* is the hindmost member of the quarter muscles and is only distinctly palpable at the root of the tail where it borders the pelvic outlet and where it in part covers the posterior face of the tuber ischii (Chart Three and Fig. 38). Lower down the back of the thigh it sinks in between other muscles and attaches to the medial epicondyle of the femur.

These muscles of the hindquarters comprise the '*hamstring group*' and have basically two areas of origin. All three muscles have deep origins from the tuber ischii, but more superficial origins extend from the dorsal and lateral sacroiliac ligaments and the first two coccygeal vertebrae (Fig. 23). These muscles are extremely important in locomotion and will be mentioned again in Part Three.

While in the region of the buttocks you can notice the long flexible tail limited in front by the quarters, below by the anal opening, and by the points of the buttocks on either side. The tail has a skeleton consisting of coccygeal vertebrae (Chart One). It also has *coccygeal muscles* which can elevate, depress or incline the tail laterally. Long hairs are present except on the lower surface at the base, and are useful in dislodging flies, etc., from the hindquarters.

The inner side of the thigh presents no really distinctive characters, the skin is very thin and only attached to the underlying structures by loose fatty connective tissue. The greater part of the surface is occupied by the *sartorius muscle* in front and the *gracilis muscle* behind. These are two straps of muscle which have their primary insertions through a fascial sheet onto the medial patellar ligament. The gracilis also has attachments to the crural fascia and thus indirectly onto the tuber calcis of the hock. The front of the thigh is composed of the four parts of the *quadriceps femoris muscle* (*rectus femoris* and the tripartite *vastus*) deeply palpable through the skin and fascia lata (Fig. 38). This group of muscles covers the front and sides of the femur. The origins are from the ilium and the femur, but all four parts insert onto the patella. The patella is attached through the three *patellar ligaments* (Figs. 27 and 28) with the tibial crest and tuberosity. You can clearly feel these structures at the front of the stifle joint. The patellar ligaments are to be regarded as the tendons of the quadriceps muscle which communicate the action to the tibia, the patella being intercalated as a sesamoid bone. In the region of the stifle the musculocutaneous fold from the flank passes on to its front surface (Chart Two).

THE LEG AND HOCK

The muscles of the leg cover almost all of the tibia except its inner face which is subcutaneous. In great measure the muscles are concealed in the upper part of the leg by the lower ends and the tendinous insertions of the quarter muscles. Below the stifle joint the tibial crest is easily identified and the tibial shaft can be felt

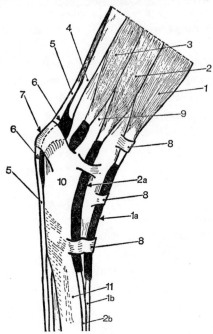

FIG. 39. Muscles, tendons and tendon sheaths of the hock in lateral view. (After Bradley.)

(1, 1a, 1b) Long digital extensor, synovial sheath and tendon. (2, 2a, 2b) Lateral digital extensor, synovial sheath and tendon. (3) Deep digital flexor tendon. (4) Gastrocnemius tendon. (5) Superficial digital flexor tendon. (6) Synovial bursa under superficial flexor tendon. (7) Tuber calcis. (8) Annular ligaments. (9) Tibia. (10) Tarsus. (11) Metatarsus.

throughout its length. As in the forearm the muscles fall into two major groups. The muscle mass in front of and on the outer side of the limb from the stifle down (the gaskin) has its origin from the extensor fossa of the femur and the lateral condyle of the tibia. These are the digital extensor muscles and the hock flexor muscles, and may assist in stifle joint fixation. The *long digital extensor muscle* arises from the lower end of the femur (extensor fossa), and lies just below the skin at the front of the second thigh giving the visible contour (Fig. 38). It can be located and felt easily. It ends in a long tendon which passes over the front of the hock within a synovial sheath. Below the hock it is joined by the tendon of the *lateral digital extensor muscle* to give a *common extensor tendon*. This passes down in front of the metatarsal bone to the third phalanx, into the extensor process of which it is inserted (Figs. 19, 21 and 39).

Beneath the long digital extensor muscle, between it and the tibial shaft, lies the *tibialis anterior muscle*. This hock flexor is composed of ordinary muscle tissue with muscle fibres arising actually from the tibial shaft. At the lower end of the tibia it is succeeded by a tendon which divides. One part of the tendon is inserted into the head of the metatarsal bone, the other into the fused first and second tarsal bones of the hock. We are aware that hock flexion is synchronous with stifle flexion and that when one of these joints extends the other does likewise. A muscle which has an important bearing on this 'reciprocal mechanism' is sandwiched between the long digital extensor and the anterior tibial muscles. It is the tendinous, cord-like *peroneus tertius muscle* which arises from the lower end of the femur in common with the long digital extensor muscle. In its course down the leg it rests on the tibialis anterior muscle. Immediately above the front of the hock joint the tendinous cord bifurcates. One branch is inserted into the head of the metatarsal bone, the other into the fourth tarsal bone of the hock. The action of the tibialis anterior is to flex the hock. The tendinous peroneus tertius plays a purely mechanical role. It synchronizes the action of the stifle and hock ensuring that the hock flexes whenever the stifle flexes. It is on this account that a horse with a straight stifle also has a straight hock and that one with a bent stifle has also a bent hock. Incidentally in a horse possessing a normal stifle and hock, a line dropped perpendicularly from the tuber ischii passes down the back of the hindleg from hock to heel.

The muscle masses at the back of the leg from the stifle down (Fig. 38) have their origin on the lower end of the back of the femur (the supracondyloid ridges and fossa), and the upper end of the back of the tibia. These areas are not palpable from the surface, being deeply covered by the lower ends of the thigh muscles, and the crural fascia. The muscles are stifle and digital flexors and hock extensors. The outline of the posterior part of the leg is formed by the belly of the *gastrocnemius muscle*. Halfway down the leg the powerful tendon begins. It is intimately associated with the tendon of the deeper lying *superficial digital flexor muscle* which is itself almost entirely tendinous. This combined tendon is palpable as a very stout cord, the *Achilles tendon* (Figs. 38 and 39). The gastrocnemius tendon attaches to the tuber calcis of the hock, while the superficial digital flexor tendon broadens and flattens to cap the tuber calcis attaching to it but then continuing down to the underside of the foot (Fig. 39). A functional entity of significance is a strong tendinous band associated with the gastrocnemius muscle passing from the femur to fuse with the tarsal tendon of the hamstring muscles. The *deep digital flexor muscle* lies close to the hind border of the tibial shaft. Its tendon running in a synovial sheath is deeply felt in the lower half of the leg in front of the Achilles tendon (Fig. 39).

The hock joint requires little more description other than that already given in Part One. The inner lip of the trochlea of the tibial tarsal can be felt as can the medial malleolus of the tibia just above it. The fibular tarsal bone can also be felt from the surface on the outer side with the prominent lateral malleolus of the tibia. Obviously the tuber calcis with the attached Achilles tendon is palpable, but of the tarsal bones none is individually identifiable.

THE METATARSUS AND DIGIT

In the metatarsus, just as in the metacarpus, the third metatarsal bone is practically entirely subcutaneous except at the back. Other features of the metatarsus and digit are closely comparable to the forelimb. The surface features which are palpable behind the cannon bone are the borders of the suspensory ligament and the deep and superficial flexor tendons. A check ligament, the *subtarsal ligament*, joins the deep flexor but is not so well developed as its equivalent in the forelimb. It is similarly a tendinous band detached from the tarsal joint capsule and attached to the deep flexor tendon.

The features of the digit below the fetlock are comparable to those of the forelimb.

PART THREE

THE HORSE AT REST AND IN MOTION

It is very seldom that the body of the horse appears completely motionless. One might possibly imagine that the horse at rest somewhat resembled a kitchen table, an oblong body propped up on four legs, one at each corner. The legs of the table are, or should be, rigid. The top of the table, its body let us say, is also an immovable structure when in use.

To help in supporting the weight of the body the limb must exert an upward thrust against the hip or shoulder. A table leg is doing just this to the corner of the table. Thus when the horse is standing at rest the sum of the vertical forces produced by the legs against the body is equal but opposite to the body weight which is acting down through the centre of gravity, and the analogy with the table still holds. However, the horse is capable of producing forward thrusts with its legs against the body, which are evidenced as horizontal forces along the body driving the animal forwards. Thus at this stage the table analogy becomes unusable.

The truth is that the only real resemblance between horse and table lies in the body, and although it would be untrue to say that the body of the horse is devoid of movement, apart from that produced either by respiration or a good shake intended to remove flies or the vestiges of bedding adherent to the skin, the range of movement is limited. Such movement as it does possess is confined to certain well defined regions of the spine as suggested in Part One. More importantly, movement of the trunk itself occurs within, or between, the forelimbs.

The thorax or rib-cage of the horse is not attached to the limbs by any firm bony union—the horse has no clavicle (collar bone)—but simply by muscular attachments between them. What is even more interesting is that the horses' body is suspended in a cradle formed of muscles, the serratus ventralis muscles, between the two scapulae (Fig. 43 in the Appendix). These embracing muscles allow the thorax to rise and fall between the horse's shoulders, or to lean over a little to one side or the other, without any corresponding deviation of either forelimb from the perpendicular. No table top can do this!

EQUILIBRIUM AND THE CENTRE OF GRAVITY

The centre of gravity varies with the individual horse, its conformation and weight distribution, and also with its attitude at the moment. The head and neck play the parts of a bob-weight on a long flexible lever. When the head is lifted the centre of gravity moves backwards; when the head is lowered it moves forwards.

Equilibrium of the body when at a standstill can only be maintained if a line dropped through the centre of gravity meets the ground within the oblong produced by joining up, with imaginary lines, the positions of the four feet on the ground. The ability on the part of the horse to lift a particular foot off the ground and still maintain its balance will depend on the relationship of the three remaining feet to the position of the centre of gravity.

The position of the centre of gravity in the stationary horse may be judged by dropping a line down from the highest point of the withers and crossing it by a second line stretching from the point of the shoulder to the point of the buttock (tuber ischii). It will be found on doing this that the centre of gravity lies nearer to the shoulders than the hips. Thus when standing quietly at rest the horse can lift one of its hindfeet off the ground and still maintain its balance. In fact the horse has a habit of resting its hindfeet alternately, allowing the fellow limb to support the body on what is a three-point suspension. This is due to the fact that the basic oblong of support mentioned above can be subdivided into two triangles of support by imaginary lines joining the right forefoot with the left hindfoot and the left forefoot with the right hindfoot. This implies that when the right hindfoot is lifted the centre of gravity lies within the triangle formed from right forefoot, left hindfoot and left forefoot. The same situation is apparent when the left hindfoot is raised.

The front 'half' of the body is a good deal heavier than the remainder as the position of the centre of gravity shows. The amount of weight resting on either forefoot of the horse is far greater than is usually imagined. If a horse weighs 10 cwt. approximately three-fifths of the weight, viz. 6 cwt. is supported by the two forefeet collectively. If one foot is lifted from the ground while the head is lowered, as when the horse is grazing, the whole 6 cwt. may be transferred to the remaining forefoot. In order to lift a foreleg and still maintain balance a considerable amount of this frontal weight must be transferred back until the centre of gravity lies behind the intersection of the diagonals of the feet. This shifting of weight within the body can be brought about by several methods. These are:

(a) Raising the head and neck above body level.

(b) Contraction of the serratus ventralis muscles attaching scapulae to ribs. Contracting together they raise the thorax relative to the forelegs which may have a slight effect on the centre of gravity. More importantly, if they contract singly the weight is shifted away from the midline of the body towards the limb on the side of the muscle acting. However, this shifting of weight cannot occur by unilateral serratus action alone, it must be accompanied by contraction of the thoracic parts of the rhomboid and trapezius muscles of the same side. These muscles pass from the upper end of the scapula, the cartilage of prolongation and the scapular spine to attach to the mid-dorsal line of the body in the region of the supraspinous ligament and ligamentum nuchae (Fig. 43 in the Appendix). These muscles will roll the thorax over towards the scapula at the same time as it is being raised. In effect this procedure allows the thorax to be raised slightly on the side on which the muscles are acting throwing extra weight onto this forefoot. This thereby takes enough weight off the opposite fore-limb to permit the elbow joint to flex and the limb to be advanced.

(c) Contraction of the anterior deep pectoral muscles extending from the sternum to the prescapular fascia will raise the thorax relative to the limbs, acting in a manner similar to the serratus ventralis muscles, also resembling these latter muscles in their unilateral action.

(d) Flexion of one or both hocks with the hindfeet planted firmly on the ground.

In a similar manner the centre of gravity may be moved forward by lowering the head and to some extent by flexing a knee. However, knee flexion is not generally practised for any purpose other than establishing or maintaining a gait, since it seriously reduces the power of support and may precipitate a fall.

THE HORSE AT A STANDSTILL

Let us now return to a further consideration of our horse at the standstill. The foregoing remarks should have shown us that the technique by which the horse produces a voluntary redistribution of weight, by means of a contraction of muscles which raise or lower the head, by unilateral action of the ventral serrate, anterior deep pectoral, rhomboid and trapezius muscles, by contraction or relaxation of limb extensors, combined with perfect synchronization of them all, is as essential to the horse standing still as it is when the horse changes from the standstill to the walk.

We must consider in more detail how a horse stands, and especially why it is that many horses are able to relax in the standing position with little fatigue? It is often stated that the horse can sleep standing, this may not be strictly true. It would be more correct to say that the horse can 'doze' whilst standing. A sound sleep must be accompanied by removal of weight from the limbs brought about by the horse lying down. Dozing may occur habitually in some horses whilst in others only occasionally, and the reason they can do this is associated with what is termed the 'stay mechanism' present in both fore- and hindlimbs (Figs. 40 and 41). This mechanism basically consists of a system of muscles and ligaments whereby the main joints can be firmly 'locked' in position and held there until 'unlocked'. At least part of the mechanism is identical in fore- and hindlimbs, and is based on the suspensory ligament running down the back of the cannon bone, often termed the 'suspensory apparatus'. The suspensory ligament divides into two branches inserted into the proximal sesamoid bones, and these are attached by ligaments to the first phalanx and also to the second phalanx (Fig. 21). The sesamoid bones are the 'patellae' of the fetlock joint, the suspensory ligament being a purely automatic elastic cord which serves as the main support for the fetlock preventing excessive dorsiflexion (overextension). The fetlock is normally 'overextended' when supporting the horses weight. The prolongation of the suspensory ligament to the front of the phalanges (Fig. 21) would appear to be a mechanism to tie down the common digital extensor tendon, acting in a similar way to the annular ligaments present in the region of the carpus and hock (Figs. 37 and 39). The suspensory ligament also serves to eliminate concussion and abruptness in the action of the fetlock during movement.

Supplementing the suspensory ligament are a pair of tendons, the superficial digital flexor and deep digital flexor, which are in effect muscles and therefore not automatic. However, they do become automatic at the limits of their extension when the check ligaments come into action to support the tendons. These check ligaments do not run, as do normal ligaments, from bone to bone, but from bone to tendon, making the tendon function as a ligament by cutting off the muscular attachment above. The superficial flexor tendons of both fore- and hindlimbs receive a check ligament above the knee or hock (from radius and tibia respectively), and the deep flexor tendons of both limbs receive a check ligament from below the knee or hock.

Thus below the knee or hock the horses limb is supported by three elastic ligaments at the back:

(1) *Suspensory ligament*, supporting the fetlock and pastern joints.
(2) *Superficial digital flexor tendon*, supporting the fetlock and pastern joints. It is muscular in the forelimb, but mainly tendinous in the hindlimb. The tendons are limited by check ligaments and when the fetlock moves down the joint is automatically supported by the check ligament and the tendon.
(3) *Deep digital flexor tendon*, supporting the fetlock, pastern and coffin joints, and like the superficial flexor it is equipped with a check ligament.

The suspensory ligament and the two digital flexor muscles operate in series. As the body weight presses down through the fetlock this joint moves down, the suspensory ligament tightens first followed by the superficial flexor and then the deep flexor tendons.

So far the stay mechanism extending from the knee or hock to the foot has been elucidated. However, the remainder of both

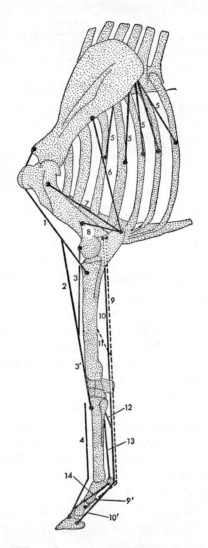

FIG. 40. Stay apparatus of the forelimb.
(1) Biceps brachii muscle. (2) Lacertus fibrosus. (3) Extensor carpi radialis muscle.
(3′) Conjoint tendon of extensor carpi radialis and lacertus fibrosus. (4) Common
digital extensor tendon. (5) Fibrous intersections in serratus ventralis muscle. (6)
Long head of triceps muscle. (7) Lateral head of triceps muscle. (8) Medial head of
triceps muscle. (9) Superficial digital flexor muscle. (9′) Tendon of superficial
digital flexor. (10) Deep digital flexor muscle. (10′) Tendon of deep digital flexor.
(11) Radial check ligament to superficial flexor tendon. (12) Carpal check ligament
to deep flexor tendon. (13) Suspensory ligament. (14) Extension of suspensory
ligament onto extensor tendon.

fore- and hindlimbs are maintained in an extended position by a system of muscles.

In the forelimb the thoracic part of the serratus ventralis muscle is the major factor attaching the limb to the body (Fig. 40). Its muscular belly is interspersed with inelastic fibrous tissue which supports the body when the muscle is relaxed. This means that the weight of the body is hanging from the upper end of the scapula and it tends to flex (close) the shoulder joint. Thus an arrangement exists to prevent shoulder flexion, composed basically of the biceps brachii muscle which extends from the scapular tuberosity to the radius. It is largely tendinous (inelastic) in nature and tension builds up in it as the shoulder tends to flex. However, this action can only occur if the biceps is prevented from flexing the elbow joint. Therefore arrangements exist to prevent the elbow from flexing, through two mechanisms:

(1) Both deep and superficial digital flexor muscles have humeral heads originating from the medial epicondyle of the humerus. This epicondyle is a relatively large projection providing a lever arm to remove the line of action of the muscles away from the centre of rotation at the articulatory surface of the elbow joint (Figs. 15 and 40). The humeral heads of both superficial and deep flexors are marked by much inelastic material. The normal standing position involves dorsiflexion of the fetlock joint which tenses the digital flexors, the inelastic parts are stretched and passive tension is built up in them to maintain elbow extension.

(2) The long head of the triceps muscle is attached to the ole-cranon process of the ulna from an origin on the posterior border of the scapula. Isometric contraction of the triceps is a key factor in the shoulder/elbow fixation mechanism.

Shoulder flexion is also prevented by isometric contraction of the supraspinatus muscle which is a major shoulder extensor attaching to the medial and lateral tuberosities of the upper end of the humerus (Fig. 13).

The knee is the remaining joint in the forelimb and in station it is predisposed to effortless weight bearing since the radius and cannon bone are in the same vertical line. It is also prevented from buckling forwards by an inelastic string inserted onto the large metacarpal bone. This is a tendon, the lacertus fibrosus, arising from the biceps tendon in the upper arm and running through the extensor carpi radialis muscle of the forearm. Thus tension built up in the biceps is transmitted through this system to assist in the fixation of the knee in extension.

In order to understand the stay mechanism of the hindlimb (often referred to as the 'reciprocal system') we must try and correlate the overall structure of the hindlimb with that of the forelimb. In the latter the scapula slopes forward and down to its junction with the upper arm at the shoulder, as the femur does to its junction with the gaskin at the stifle in the hindlimb. These two segments are the parts which actually connect the substance of the limb to the body. The upper arm bone (humerus) slopes back to the elbow joint, as the tibia does to the hock in the hindlimb. From these points the legs are similar, the hindleg descending directly to the ground, the foreleg descending with an added joint, the knee, which for our purposes is maintained unbent.

The serratus ventralis muscle of the thorax has no equivalent in the hindlimb since there is a bony attachment of the limb to the body. The biceps brachii has its equivalent in the peroneus tertius muscle, an entirely tendinous strand extending from the extensor fossa of the femur to the large metatarsal bone (Fig. 41). Weight acting downwards tends to flex the stifle, and this is in part counteracted by tension building up in the peroneus tertius. The action of this muscle on the stifle is reflected as a purely mechanical flexing action on the hock. Therefore an arrangement exists to prevent the hock from flexing through the gastrocnemius muscle attached to the tuber calcis from an origin on the lower end of the femur. This is only an active extensor when the foot is off the ground. When standing, the muscle is a passive extensor of the hock since incorporated into it is a tendinous band which combines (in mechanical action) with the almost entirely tendinous superficial digital flexor muscle. During standing it relieves the constant strain otherwise imposed on the gastrocnemius, and maintains the hock in extension. The overall action is that there is a purely mechanical opposition between the peroneus tertius and the tendoligamentous system of the superficial flexor and tendinous part of the gastrocnemius. This means that should the tibialis anterior muscle contract to flex the hock, the reciprocal system will flex the stifle, and should the gastrocnemius muscle contract to extend the hock, the reciprocal system will

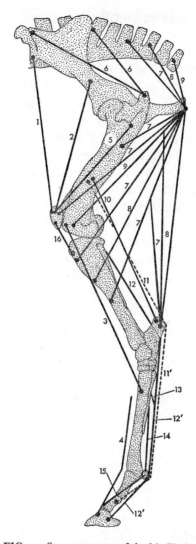

FIG. 41. Stay apparatus of the hindlimb.
(1) Tensor fasciae latae muscle. (2) Rectus femoris muscle. (3) Peroneus tertius muscle. (4) Common digital extensor tendon. (5) Vastus muscles. (6) Gluteal muscles. (7) Biceps femoris muscle. (8) Semitendinosus muscle. (9) Semimembranosus muscle. (10) Gastrocnemius muscle. (11) Superficial digital flexor muscle. (11′) Tendon of superficial digital flexor. (12) Deep digital flexor muscle. (12′) Tendon of deep digital flexor. (13) Tarsal check ligament to the deep flexor tendon. (14) Suspensory ligament. (15) Extension of suspensory ligament onto extensor tendon. (16) Patellar ligament.

extend the stifle. One cannot flex or extend without the other
following suit.

In order for this reciprocal action of the stifle and hock to
function adequately in the standing position the stifle must first
be fixed in an extended position. This stifle fixation could theoreti-
cally be brought about by contraction of the quadriceps femoris
muscle group which inserts onto the tibia through the patellar
ligaments and patella. However, a strong contraction of the
biceps femoris and semitendinosus muscles (the major components
of the 'hamstring' group), as they attach to the patella, will fix
the stifle in the standing position with no detectable contraction
of the quadriceps femoris muscles. The biceps femoris muscle
with attachments to the back of the femur and to the patella
will extend the hip joint and pull on the patella sliding it up the
femoral trochlea. The patella and the medial patellar ligament
may even engage with the upper end of the inner trochlear ridge
and become locked in position, the stifle consequently being
locked by the straight patellar ligaments in an extended position
(Fig. 28B). The greater the weight then falling on the limb at the
head of the femur the greater the tendency to flex the hip and the
tighter is the lock. In this situation little or no muscular effort is
required to maintain posture. In order to 'unlock' the system,
the quadriceps femoris muscle mass may contract, lifting the
patella, while the biceps femoris muscle contracts to pull the
patella laterally off the ridge. Contraction of the tensor fasciae
latae muscle may also assist in the unlocking mechanism by lifting
and pulling the patella laterally.

The importance of the fascia, the dense connective tissue which
surrounds and binds up the muscles, especially in the forearm
and second thigh has not been specifically mentioned. This fascia
confines the muscles thus directing their actions; also the fascia
may become organised into distinct areas for holding down muscle
tendons in the region of joints. This is seen in the annular ligaments
which bind down the extensor tendons and the peroneus tertius
and tibialis anterior muscles to the front of the tibia, hock and
metatarsus. Finally the fascia may actually be utilised as a tendon
of muscle attachment, especially noticeable in the gaskin where
the tarsal tendon of the biceps femoris and semitendinosus muscles
attaches to the tuber calcis, this tendon being modified fascia.

Likewise, the tendinous band running along with the gastroc-nemius muscle and having an important role in the reciprocal mechanism, is formed from modified fascia and is incorporated into the tarsal tendon above the hock. The fascia then plays an important part in giving assistance to the constant strain imposed on the muscles of the limb.

It must not be thought that the ability of these muscular combinations to convert four highly motile limbs into solid props at a moments notice, or to relax them even more rapidly, is governed by voluntary muscle control alone; nor that these changes in function are brought about entirely automatically.

The newly born foal, an hour or two after its arrival, will be able in most instances to stand up and follow its mother without any preliminary training such as a human infant would receive for at least the first eighteen months of its life. It would appear therefore that greater and more rapidly acquired ability to stand goes with four legs than with a single pair. It could, however, be argued that while the human infant has to learn voluntary muscle control, the foal comes into the world with an inborn capacity for reflex or automatic control of its limbs which can only be possessed by a four-legged animal, or at least by one which does not have to maintain the upright stance. One would think that all the human infant would have to do is throw its body weight forward and place each of its two feet forward, the one in front of the other, in time to prevent falling on its own face. But the snag is that the human infant has first to learn how to straighten the body, which is able to bend in every direction through possessing a highly flexible spine, and maintain its rigidity. Not until this has been accomplished can the body be balanced while the child learns to use its limbs. The foal has an almost rigid body and it would seem to be easier to maintain balance on four limbs so long as the standing position is maintained.

When it starts to follow its mother shortly after birth the two forelimbs and the two hindlimbs have not only to move forward but also they have to synchronize very accurately and with perfect timing and this they prove themselves highly capable of achieving in many instances. It would seem that this could only be effected if there existed in the brain a control centre in full charge of locomotory procedure.

T.H.—K

The whole process of movement upon four legs through a series of varying gaits is a far too complicated procedure to be acquired by a foal even within an hour or two of birth, and the responses are far more rapid than any which could be achieved by reasoning. There is little doubt that the horse's 'proprioceptive sense', its ability to assess the position of the various parts of its body and relate them to both space and solid surrounding objects, plays a considerable part in the ability of foals to stand at a remarkably early age and follow their mothers, in order to obtain sustenance, rather than lie in one place and wait for it to be brought to them. Another factor is that foals are carried for rather a lengthy period in their mother's wombs and are delivered in an advanced stage of development. A human baby is carried nearly as long, but is delivered still in a state of 'foetalization', very underdeveloped, and having need of a considerable period of extra-uterine development before it attains anything like the stage of activity and intelligence encountered in a newly born foal.

In spite of the stay mechanisms of the limbs provided by the muscles, tendons and ligaments, these would have little value in preventing collapse of the limbs if the muscles specified could not be maintained in a state of contraction. The degree to which this occurs is conditioned by the activity of the opposing muscles. This leads one to think that a moderate degree of contraction, at least, must be maintained during dozing in both the extensors and flexors of the shoulder, elbow, hip and stifle joints. How this is effected is not easy to understand unless a special centre in the brain takes control of the stay mechanism. However, horses falling deeply asleep or placed under anaesthesia while still standing do not remain in this position, but double up at the knees and hocks and fall to the ground, if not controlled and let down gently.

MOVING OFF

Now, although a foal may be able to stand within an hour or two of birth, it is still a little puzzled by the anatomical features of its own limbs, especially the forelimbs. It may need a little time, perhaps only a few minutes, to discover how it gets out of its straight limbed position and can move one forefoot in front of the other, in other words how it walks. Anyone watching a foal when it rises for the first time may observe this indecision which disappears after one or two successful starts. An adult horse has long since learned the trick of moving off from a standstill, but for a foal the matter is not immediately quite so easy. It has to discover for itself that it can move a forelimb upon which its weight is resting only by adopting a special attitude or by making some kind of movement which momentarily raises the weight from a forefoot and liberates the joints so that they can move freely, always in a straight line.

As we have already seen, the adult horse effects this forelimb freedom by a variety of means, all directed towards shifting the centre of gravity backwards. The weight which originally fell upon the forefoot is now in great part transferred to the hindfoot, or feet as the case may be. The actual degree of movement necessary to effect this weight transfer is very slight and not at all obvious. Even when an almost imperceptible hock flexion occurs and the tail end of the body sinks an inch or so towards the ground, it may release anything between a half and two hundredweight from a forefoot and transfer it to the hindfeet.

In order to lift a forefoot from the ground the shoulder and elbow will first have to flex. Shoulder flexion is brought about by contraction of several muscles, notably the deltoid, teres minor and teres major muscles. These latter two insert on the humerus from an origin on the posterior border of the scapula (Fig. 36). Flexion of the elbow joint is brought about by biceps muscle contraction acting through its own insertion onto the upper end of the radius, together with contraction of the brachialis muscle which has an origin from the humerus and an insertion on the radius along with the biceps. At the same time the triceps muscle is relaxing permitting the biceps to assume supremacy. The knee moves forwards and upwards thus raising the foot from the ground, while simultaneously the flexors at the back of the limb contract to flex the knee and digital joints. The foot is now suspended from the withers through the dorsal scapular ligament (arising from the third, fourth and fifth thoracic spines and attaching to the scapula along with the rhomboideus muscle), and the tendinous middle part of the trapezius muscle attached to the scapular spine. These together support the whole forelimb when the foot is off the ground and the limb hanging.

The limb must now be brought forwards (protracted), mainly by the action of the brachiocephalic muscle and the thoracic part of the serratus ventralis muscle. Thus the latter pulls the upper end of the scapula down and back, while the former pulls the lower part of the humerus forwards. After the limb has advanced sufficiently it is straightened again. The shoulder joint is extended mainly by the action of the supraspinatus muscle; the elbow joint by triceps muscle action on the olecranon process of the ulna. The carpus moves into extension as do the coffin, pastern and fetlock joints by contraction of the carpal and digital extensors. The coffin and pastern joints appear to overextend (dorsiflex) by the action, at the last moment, of the common digital extensor muscle. This contraction of the extensor muscle causes a build up of tension in the superficial and deep flexor tendons and their check ligaments. As backward movement (retraction) of the leg begins, the common extensor muscle slackens and the elastic rebound of the superficial and deep flexor tendons aligns the coffin and pastern joints in their contact (impact) position with the ground. No active flexor muscle action is apparently required for proper hoof placement, simply elastic rebound of the flexor tendons against the common extensor tendon being sufficient.

At the moment of impact of the foot with the ground the fore-limb has already been somewhat retracted and is in an extended position with none of the joints undergoing rotation, the limb being rigid. The real work begins now for the body has to pass over the limb while the leg remains fixed to the ground at the foot and the limb from elbow to ground remains rigid. *From this moment on when we talk of limb retraction we are implying rather that the body is being protracted (moved forwards) in relation to the limb which is fixed to the ground.*

The mechanism of the forward stride may be likened to a wheel in which the shoulder is the rim, the remainder of the limb the spoke, and the foot resting on the ground the hub. The action is dependent upon the foot being able to plant itself firmly on the ground, from, or over, which it must not slip. In other words the spoke must be solidly attached to the hub. If the foot failed to maintain its hold upon the ground either because its frog was inefficient, its shoe highly polished, or if the ground itself were wet and slippery, the leg would tend to slip backward. But when the foot can grip the ground securely it acts as a fixed fulcrum, and in this case the impetus of the body turning above the foot actually drives the body forwards.

Once the foot is on the ground and carrying weight, the shoulder and elbow are fixed by the simultaneous contraction of the biceps and triceps (extensor and flexor). Backward movement of the limb, or the propulsive phase, is brought about by the contraction of several extrinsic muscles moving the forelimb as a rigid frame rotating around the muscular attachments of the scapula to the thorax. Thus the latissimus dorsi muscle and the major part of the deep pectoral muscle pull the humerus back, while the cervical part of the serratus ventralis muscle, the rhomboideus muscle and the anterior deep pectoral muscle pull the upper end of the scapula forwards (Fig. 36). These actions rotate the body forwards on the lever arm provided by the rigid leg, the fulcrum being the attachment of the hoof to the ground.

The actual propulsive force applied to the body occurs after the limb has passed the vertical, i.e. when the horse's shoulder has travelled onwards past the level of the foot. During limb retraction back to the vertical, the first half of the stride, the kinetic energy of the impact force, and the weight of the body exerting a downward force on the limb, are absorbed by several anti-concussion and weight supporting mechanisms of the foreleg. In the limb the kinetic energy is stored as potential energy of displacement and reappears as kinetic energy during the second half of the stride where it imparts forward momentum to the body. This release of stored energy within muscles which have come under tension aids in joint extension.

At the moment of contact with the ground the centre of gravity, through the tendinous thoracic part of the serratus ventralis muscle, tends to pull the scapula down and back, which in turn pulls the humerus towards the vertical. The tendency for the shoulder joint to close (flex) is resisted by the tendinous biceps muscle in front, and the tendency for the elbow to flex is resisted by the triceps muscle behind. Thus, just as in the standing position, the strong pull of the triceps and the elastic resistance of the biceps aid in the stabilization of the elbow joint during propulsion. We have then a system pivoting on an axle at about the mid-point of the upper arm which provides for smooth energy conversion.

It 'gives' down and back at impact storing kinetic energy as potential energy of displacement of the scapula and humerus in the biceps, triceps, rhomboideus and cervical part of the serratus ventralis muscles (evidenced as increased tension in these muscles). The angle behind the shoulder joint closes (flexes) by up to 20 degrees between impact and mid-stride (limb vertical) due to this mechanism. As the limb passes the vertical it is no longer solely a weight supporter but it becomes a propulsive strut and much of the weight is taken off it. Thus the energy absorbing mechanism reverses in direction and gives up its stored energy which aids in shoulder and elbow extension, together with active contraction of the extensors of these two joints.

These actions of joint extension, together with the action of the extrinsic limb retractor muscles, means that *the limb is used as an extensible propulsive strut by the muscles extending the joints, and as a propulsive lever by the muscles moving the limb as a whole.*

When the forefoot accepts weight the point of the fetlock sinks towards the ground. This movement is suitably checked, first by the suspensory ligament passing from behind the knee to the proximal sesamoid bones; then by the superficial flexor tendon inserted into the back of the first phalanx; next by the deep flexor tendon inserted into the third phalanx; lastly by the pull of the check ligaments inserted into the tendons of the superficial and deep flexors. This is a mechanism to reduce shock but mainly to add smoothness to the action. The fetlock is extended so that the phalanges are in a straight line with the leg when the foot contacts the ground. It then 'overextends' as the body weight comes onto the limb and recovers after the leg has passed the vertical. By this process the horse's limb is shortened and lengthened and this helps to keep the body at nearly the same level throughout its stride.

The action of the fetlock joint straightening from a dorsiflexed position after weight is removed from the limb provides another important additional source of forward propulsive thrust by adding this additional joint to the limb. In the consideration of the stay apparatus we saw that as the fetlock sinks towards the ground it is supported by the three structures at the back of the cannon bone, the suspensory ligament and the superficial and deep flexor tendons. Upward and forward fetlock movement is aided by the natural elasticity of the suspensory ligament, also kinetic energy is stored as potential energy of displacement in the flexor tendons and reappears as kinetic energy to move the fetlock. Most importantly the powerful deep flexor muscle pulls the third phalanx back with such energy that rotation of the coffin joint and upward movement of the fetlock imparts considerable propulsive action to the leg.

When the hoof leaves the ground at push-off, the triceps relaxes and the elastic rebound of the biceps tendon pulls the lower end of the humerus forwards. At the same time the rhomboideus and the cervical part of the serratus ventralis muscles are relaxing permitting elastic rebound of the tendinous thoracic part of the serratus ventralis. With these mechanisms the process of swinging the limb forwards is begun.

We can now consider briefly how a horse starts off from a standstill when emerging from a starting gate or galloping away from the spot on which it has been standing, simply because something has frightened it. It gives a sudden push with both hindfeet against the ground. In some instances the backward and downward movement of the hindfeet may be so impulsive it amounts to a stamp, quite noisy in fact. The amount of propulsion resulting will depend a great deal upon the ground surface beneath the hindfeet. If the ground is greasy or slippery from rain or ice, the horse may not move forwards at all. The backward force the horse can exert is limited by the nature of the ground surface as well as by the weight of the body the animal has to shift. In addition, weather conditions may play a part. The body of the horse usually offers a marked resistance to wind and the horse has a strong dislike of a headwind accompanied by rain!

It may be noticed that when the horse gives this sudden stamp upon the ground with its hindfeet it results in an uprising of the front end of the body, almost as though the horse contemplated rearing in the air. The thrust is made against the ground at the rear end of the horse, but the weight of the horse's body and its inertia at the time causes the animal's front part to lift because the long sides and prominent hips set up a considerable resistance to the air stream they encounter. The lifting of the front end of the body throws weight onto the hindfeet, with the result that the hocks flex, together with the stifles. When, acting under the influence of fear, the horse again pushes its hindfeet hard against the ground and the hocks and stifles straighten, together with the hips, the body is propelled forwards. As the forefeet are by now off the ground, they cannot assist in propulsion, so the body continues to shoot forwards and upwards according to the force exerted against the ground. An animal preparing to accelerate rapidly without raising its front feet high off the ground must start by moving the centre of gravity of the body forwards relative to its hips and shoulders in order to generate a maximum drive.

The push against the ground by both hindfeet is effected by the hamstring muscles (biceps femoris, semitendinosus and semi-membranosus) together with the gastrocnemius and deep digital flexor, and the quadriceps femoris group of muscles exerting their pull on the stifle through the patella and patellar ligaments. If the ground beneath the hindfeet is firm and unyielding, the force exerted upon the lower limbs by the sudden straightening of hips, stifles and hocks will take effect on the body. In other circum-stances the hindfeet may 'skid' backwards and the forelimbs come to earth again to restore balance.

So far sufficient information has been given to enable us to look more closely at two important attributes of muscle action, both involving the concept of 'cooperative antagonism' of muscles. On contraction of the limb muscles movement of the body as a whole may or may not occur. When movement does occur the muscles involved must be able to accelerate and retard the action. When movement does not occur these same muscles must exert forces which will balance the forces present (both horizontal and vertical) and thus prevent rotation of the levers bringing about movement.

From this last statement it is clear that as long as the animal is not lying down the muscles of the limbs are in constant action to maintain the standing position or to bring about movement. Therefore to keep the forelimb rigid a stream of nervous impulses must be passing to the shoulder extensors (biceps) and the elbow extensors (triceps). As well as their major actions the biceps opposes flexing of the shoulder by the triceps, and the triceps opposes elbow flexion by the biceps. At the same time the biceps is actively aiding the extensors of the knee through the lacertus fibrosus and extensor carpi radialis tendon, which are resisting the flexors of the knee and digit both superficial and deep.

Many of the above mentioned muscles which are cooperating in standing must, during movement, be antagonistic to one another. During limb retraction, for instance, the limb is straightened at all of the joints. Shoulder extension is brought about in part by triceps relaxation, but mainly the biceps, by muscular action and elastic recoil, extends the joint. The triceps referred to here is the long head of the triceps originating on the scapula. At the same time as this is relaxing to allow the shoulder joint to extend, the two short heads of the triceps from the rear of the humerus are actively contracting to extend the elbow and aid in shoulder extension by mechanical action through the biceps. During shoulder and elbow extension the long head of the triceps does not simply relax, it eases off in its contraction allowing the biceps to obtain supremacy, but still exerting sufficient resistance to prevent the joint from being too suddenly straightened. Were it not for this cooperative antagonism between muscles, the joints may dislocate, the ligaments being torn by overextension of the joints. It is this synchronization of muscles on either side of a limb which makes smooth operation of a joint a practical possibility. Accurate timing of the opposing action is also essential, for in its absence large bones like the humerus or femur and small bones like the proximal sesamoids, the navicular bone or even the second phalanges, may be completely shattered.

COMING TO EARTH

Horses were originally designed to operate on marshy ground, and until such time as the competition became too keen they got on very well on four toes, although probably only three of these made contact with the ground, with expandable footpads which kept them from sinking in the marshes. The foot of the modern horse would not have been of great service then, partly because the diameter of the sole is much greater than that of the pastern and this would make it difficult to extricate a foot once submerged in the mud.

There are certain features and mechanisms in the limbs which serve to accept and dissipate weight both during normal standing and when the foot contacts the ground during movement. The horse in motion normally drops its weight on the heel first, but at rest the weight is accepted mainly on the wall and the frog. In the standing position body weight acts down through the limb bones to the tip of the third phalanx. This contacts the inner surface of the sole just in front of the apex of the frog (Fig. 19). Normally, and in the absence of inflammation, the third phalanx is prevented from digging down into and penetrating the sole by the fact that it is attached to the inner surface of the wall of the foot by approximately 600 laminae. These are minute plates attached to the periosteum covering the third phalanx, which interleave with similar laminae on the inner surface of the foot wall. These laminae help to absorb shock upon contact of the foot with the ground, and also spread the weight from the quite small area of the sole in front of the frog to the frog and the wall. If we remember that the sole of the foot is concave and in addition that it is further raised from the ground by the thickness of a shoe or plate, we can begin to realize the strain that must be thrown upon the comparatively small third phalanx by this everlasting pull upon its sensitive periosteum.

When a horse lands from a jump onto firm ground one forefoot comes to earth, usually first settling on its heel. As the body travels over the stationary foot the toe and the quarters of the foot come into contact with the ground. Fortunately the sole is able to descend slightly without incurring injury, and this not only saves the sole but also plays a useful part in limiting the effects of concussion. At impact the heels expand to distribute concussion, weight acting down through the limb presses the second phalanx down and back against the digital cushion which in turn presses the frog down against the ground. The cushion is compressed and expands on either side to press against the lateral cartilages of the third phalanx further spreading the thin walls of the quarters. The digital cushion can only be fully efficient when the horny frog is left sufficiently untrimmed to enable it to make contact with the ground. The cartilages move outwards and compress the coronary plexus of veins pumping blood up the limb. At the same time blood is partially held in the vascular plexus within the foot by the pressing of the lateral cartilages against the coronary plexus. This forms a hydraulic cushion of blood for the third phalanx which aids in reducing concussion.

All of the limb joints possess some degree of concussion absorbing or dissipating action, and the yielding of the shoulder and elbow joints on impact has been noticed. At the coffin joint direct concussion is partially avoided by distributing weight from the second phalanx to the navicular bone, and thus onto the third phalanx. The navicular is supported by the deep flexor tendon, and the greatest pressure between these two structures occurs when the body weight passes over the foot and the fetlock is moving down towards the ground rotating the coffin joint. At the fetlock joint the suspensory apparatus helps to change the direction of concussive forces and weight distribution, and additional support is afforded by the flexor tendons. The carpal and hock joints both function as mechanical shock absorbing mechanisms, greatly reducing concussion.

THE NEXT STEP

We will now presume that our foal has 'found its feet' and is capable of advancing a forelimb and setting its foot firmly on the ground. Its natural instinct, and the need to form a three-point suspension, will induce it to advance the diagonally placed hindfoot and a rearrangement of the centre of gravity is unnecessary. The action of the hindlimb resembles the forelimb in that the leg is protracted and brought to the ground from which point it serves as a rigid spoke until past the vertical at which stage joint extension occurs.

Hindlimb protraction is brought about initially by flexion of the hip joint which will carry the femur and stifle forward. In spite, however, of all that has been written about the degree of movement (in every direction except abduction) developed by the femur, the amount in reality is very limited. Femur movement in the horse, quite unlike that in the dog, is limited by the heavy thigh muscles and by the close attachment of the thigh to the horse's body. This will obviously be the limiting factor in the length of the horse's stride. These hip flexors are in the main deeply lying muscles running from the underside of the lumbar vertebrae onto the upper end of the femur (e.g. psoas minor and iliacus). However, certain superficial muscles do have some flexing action, notably the superficial gluteal, sartorius and tensor fasciae latae.

At the same time as the hip is being flexed the stifle is also flexed by the action of parts of the biceps femoris and semitendinosus muscles which have insertions onto the tibia in the region of the tibial crest and tuberosity. In turn this stifle flexion will bring about hock flexion through the mechanical action of the peroneus tertius. In addition, contraction of the tibialis anterior muscle will bring about hock flexion directly and stifle flexion indirectly through the tendinous cord of the superficial flexor muscle and the tendinous part of the gastrocnemius muscle connecting the tuber calcis with the lower end of the femur. The superficial flexor at the same time, by a purely mechanical action, flexes the digit. Unlike the forelimb the superficial flexor muscle of the hindleg is almost entirely tendinous and therefore serves a largely passive, ligamentous role.

After the limb has been advanced sufficiently the stifle joint commences to extend through the action of the quadriceps femoris group of muscles. The reciprocal mechanism through the tendinous superficial flexor and tendinous cord in the gastrocnemius extends the hock joint simultaneously. The digit also extends as the extension of the hock in some measure relaxes the superficial flexor tendon. The common digital extensor muscles act in the same manner as those of the foreleg already described.

The hip-stifle-hock system means that when the foot contacts the ground the hindleg is locked into a rigid spoke. Retraction is begun by contraction of extrinsic muscles of the quarters and thighs. The biceps femoris, semitendinosus, semimembranosus and part of the gracilis, pull the rigid limb backwards by their attachments to the back of the femur and tibia, and through the tarsal tendon to the tuber calcis of the hock. At the same time, by the insertion of the biceps femoris onto the patella, they strongly stabilize the stifle joint, and thus the hock joint through the reciprocal mechanism. Muscles of the rump, the middle gluteals, also turn the limb on the head of the femur, extending the hip joint. Muscles of the second thigh, especially the gastrocnemius, pull on the tuber calcis along with the biceps femoris.

The limb is retracted and as it approaches the vertical the stifle and hock flex slightly subserving shock absorption and storing up kinetic energy as potential energy of displacement of the femur.

The femur therefore moves towards the vertical without lifting the weight of the hindquarters against gravity. The fetlock sinks towards the ground just as in the forelimb. As soon as the limb passes the vertical the potential energy of displacement is reconverted back into kinetic energy which aids in the extension of the hock, stifle and fetlock joints. The stifle is actively extended through quadriceps femoris action on the patella, and the rump and hamstring muscles extend the hip, stifle and hock joints with considerable power. The hock also extends through the medium of the reciprocal system and by active contraction of the gastrocnemius muscle supplementing the major pull on the tuber calcis by the tarsal tendon of the biceps femoris and semitendinosus. The deep flexor muscle is large and powerful and is the main component involved in the active straightening of the fetlock joint, whilst at the same time aiding in straightening the hock.

When the leg is fully extended, a taut line runs down from the tuber coxae (haunch) to the stifle, the tensor fasciae latae muscle, acting as a check to prevent overstretching of the leg joints. As soon as the hoof clears the ground at the end of the stride, the peroneus tertius/tibialis anterior system, by elastic rebound, snaps the hock back into semiflexion along with the stifle through the reciprocal system. The limb is then ready to be brought forward again.

We thus have a situation which is comparable to the shoulder/elbow system, acting on the rigid limb. The quadriceps femoris and peroneus tertius function like the biceps brachii; the biceps femoris and gastrocnemius function like the triceps. However, in the hindlimb the situation is simpler from the point of view of muscular cooperation since much of the action is purely mechanical. A stream of nervous impulses pass to the stifle extensors, the quadriceps group, which are resisting the stifle flexors, the biceps femoris and semitendinosus. The latter are acting mainly on the hock joint which cannot be flexed as long as the stifle remains extended due to the mechanical tendoligaments of the peroneus tertius and superficial flexor. This relieves the constant strain which would otherwise be imposed on the gastrocnemius muscle and maintains the hock extended. The hock is also maintained in an extended state by the passive action of the gastrocnemius. Active contraction of the gastrocnemius muscle aids in hock extension when the limb is off the ground and not supporting weight. The cooperative antagonism of these muscles is evident from the above account, and is also in evidence during movement of the limb. Thus when the gastrocnemius is doing its utmost to contract to extend the hock joint, as in the final phase of limb protraction prior to impact of the foot with the ground, the tibialis anterior is exerting sufficient resistance to prevent the hock being too violently straightened.

At this point we may digress a little to discuss muscle action in more general terms. The majority of muscles produce results by acting across a joint and tending to move one member of the joint on the other. The distribution of weight on the bones will result in them being used as levers. However, when movement is not required these same muscles must exert forces which will balance the forces present and prevent the levers from rotating. In many instances limb muscles are applied along the length of the limb, the muscles lying practically parallel with the lever arm. This factor may help to explain the fact that in the region of the joints various projections (tuber calcis, olecranon process) and extra bones (patella, sesamoids) are produced. These bony factors remove the power arm of the muscles further from the centre of rotation of the joint thus increasing the mechanical advantage at which the muscles work. This means that the force exerted by muscular contraction is increased as the line of direction of muscular action is moved further away from the axis of the joint, but the speed of action diminishes. The muscular force applied is not necessarily equal to the resulting force of action, in fact the object of the lever arm system is that a small force applied at the end of a long lever arm can be made to produce a much greater force near the fulcrum.

In the case of the tuber calcis of the hock the leverage provided by the muscles making up the Achilles tendon (biceps femoris and semitendinosus through the tarsal tendon, the gastrocnemius and superficial flexor) is sufficiently great to aid in the propulsion of up to half a ton of body high into the air. The lever in this instance is one in which the fulcrum is the foot in contact with the ground, the weight bears downwards on the hock joint and the muscular pull is applied to a rod, the tuber calcis, which projects 4 inches behind and above the hock. The whole digit acts as a single lever.

The same situation exists in the forelimb with the olecranon process and the triceps muscle.

There is a limit to the speed at which muscles can contract, thus the speed of the action which is mediated is also limited. A larger muscle, or several extra muscles acting around the same joint, will increase the power available but not the speed of movement. With the system of levers operating as described the foot moves very much faster through space than the tuber calcis or the olecranon process which are transmitting the power. The longer the lever arm of the tuber calcis or the olecranon process the more power is produced. On the other hand the longer the cannons and pasterns the lever arm of speed increases and relatively the lever arm of power shortens lessening the power and increasing the speed. From this it would appear that a short, thick second thigh, with hocks carried high, a long cannon bone and hind pastern straight rather than markedly oblique, should provide a greater speed than would be the case if the hock were set low and the cannon short. Against this is the fact that a longer cannon demands long flexor tendons, and a long suspensory ligament, more inclined to stress and strain, and possibly more liable to result in ultimate breakdown than when the space between the point of the hock and the fetlock joint is shorter.

ON THE WAY

Walking on four legs, as on two, becomes, after the body has been set in motion, a matter of placing the appropriate foot in the position best calculated to keep the animal from tumbling forward. For complete balance to be maintained when the animal is in motion, at least three feet must be on the ground at all phases of movement and the centre of gravity must fall within the triangle created by the supporting feet. Only one sequence of limb movements ensures that this situation occurs (the letters denote the limbs, e.g. LF .. Left forelimb):

LF   RH   RF   LH

Each foot must be lifted as soon as the one next ahead of it in the sequence contacts the ground. As a general rule each time a hindfoot comes to the ground the quarter of that side sinks a little, the hock and stifle flexing slightly and the way is now clear for a forelimb to move forward. The foot movements can be summarised by the following statements:

(1) A forefoot can be lifted when the centre of gravity lies behind the diagonal joining the other forefoot with the hindfoot of the opposite side.

(2) A hindfoot can be lifted when the centre of gravity lies in front of the diagonal joining the other hindfoot with the forefoot of the opposite side.

Three-point suspension however, is employed by the horse only during the slow walk, a gait to which few horses are at all partial. So long as the horse is moving at the slow walk, the basic conditions for stability are the same as those applying to the stationary horse. This limb sequence is also the only one enabling a slowly moving horse to stop at any instant without falling over.

CHANGE OF GAIT

During the walk the horse is supported on a three-point base, with three feet on the ground at any particular moment and the fourth raised from the ground. It therefore follows that the centre of gravity in the walking horse must lie somewhere within a triangle formed by drawing lines to pass through the horse's three feet at any particular moment touching the ground. It is only when this three-point system is effective that the horse can pull up without risk of stumbling with the fourth foot raised and independent of its stay mechanism, which gave the limb rigidity when it was asked to support weight.

The speed of the walk increases in the horse as the frequency of the limb movements increases. This implies that the length of time a limb is in contact with the ground decreases, both absolutely and also relative to the length of time that the limb is suspended. Thus the pattern of the faster walk demands that each foot shall be lifted before the foot following it in the sequence actually touches the ground. The three-point suspension maintained during the slow walk has to give way to a situation in which at certain times only two feet are left on the ground. The body is alternately supported by both limbs of one side, and then by a pair of diagonal limbs. This is the situation in the normal walk of the horse.

Two-point suspension does not provide the same stability of the body as three-point, with the result that the body rolls or tips slightly forward during the momentary failure of support, but its equilibrium is restored when the next descending foot touches the ground. The period of two-point suspension is always followed by one of three-point suspension. Thus during the normal walk there are periods of instability in the sequence of limb movements when only two limbs are on the ground.

The speed of the walk can be further increased and as soon as the period of time required for limb protraction equals that for limb retraction there will be only two limbs on the ground at the same time but never more. With still further increase in the relative duration of the protraction phase there can be periods when only one foot is on the ground. We have now reached the somewhat surprising conclusion that *the longer the limbs are off the ground relative to the length of time during which they are on the ground and exerting a forward propulsive thrust, the faster the horse is propelled.* However, the retractor muscles work well below their maximum power output when moving slowly, and increased speed is brought about by an increased power output by these retractor muscles.

FASTER

When the gait changes from a walk to a trot there is a carry-over of the two-point suspension pattern. The essential feature being that the two supporting feet are diagonals. In a fully synchronized trot a forelimb and its diagonal hindlimb work together to thrust the body forwards. As the speed of the trot increases the tendency is for only one foot to be on the ground at any time. In horses engaged in trotting matches in harness the camera often catches phases in which all four feet are off the ground with the horse still trotting. Thus there is a period during which the body is in the air with no feet on the ground, the body returns to earth onto the other two diagonal feet, which repeat the movement. The only real difference between the tracks left by a walking and a trotting horse lies in the interval between the feet, i.e. the length of stride. All that keeps a fast trotter on its feet is the ability to place the right foot in the right spot at the right time. If anything impedes the limb movement such as a stumble or some sudden interruption, the diagonally situated foot is unable to make the necessary correction in time. When the risk is foreseen the horse's best chance lies in a calculated change of action of the other limb on the same side, but unless the stumble occurs when the foot of this limb is actually off the ground the prospect of saving a fall is greatly lessened.

If a horse is trotted, or in fact walked, on soft ground it may be observed that the imprint of the hindfeet actually overlap those of the forefeet, i.e. there is a danger of interference between fore- and hindfeet. This occurs because the forefoot was raised before the hindfoot had reached the ground. Had the forefoot been even a fraction of a second later in raising, the footmarks would not have overlapped and the inner rim of the toe of the hindshoe might easily have scooped a fragment of skin off the heel of the forefoot. This is a common cause of 'over-reach'. Incidentally, while on the topic of interference between various parts of the body during movement, we can notice that the stifle joint must also be able to clear the side of the abdomen when it is brought forward. Out- ward joint rotation occurs at the hip as it flexes when the hind- limb is being brought forwards. This outward rotation is trans- mitted to the lower end of the femur thus turning the stifle outwards and helping it clear the side of the flank.

A proportion of trotting horses are apt to exaggerate the bilateral suspension phase of the walk rather than the diagonal phase, with the result that the horse 'racks' or 'paces' according to the type of action it favours. The rack is more precarious than the trot since the centre of gravity tends to be shifted from side to side imparting a rolling effect to the body. However, it does have the advantage of there being no interference between fore- and hindfeet. The rack therefore illustrates well the bilateral phases of instability in many gaits, leading to side to side oscillations of the body as it is supported alternately by right and left leg pairs. For speed to be built up with the least expenditure of energy this oscillation must be damped. The damping is in large part performed by bringing the feet as nearly as possible under the mid-line of the body, and in a very fast gallop the foot prints lie in a true line.

The general belief that the forelimbs provide support, serving to keep the horse on its feet, while the hindlimbs provide the propulsion is not wholly true. While the hindlimbs really keep the moving body in progress at a speed no greater than that at which the limbs themselves can travel in a backward direction, the forelimbs do play a very great part in driving the body forward. This is particularly so when the shoulder is obliquely placed and therefore capable of providing a longer forward stride. The stride is also increased when the forearm is long thus creating a longer spoke for the hypothetical wheel. In the hindlimb, on the other hand, a long tibia with a low hock and possibly a short cannon, shorten the lever arm and involve extra angulation of the stifle and hock, with the result that the hindfoot comes too far behind the body.

To produce optimum results the hindfoot should be beating its toe against the ground in an arc commencing just in front of the perpendicular, and for a short distance behind it. The drive is then being applied directly to the hindquarters then through the spine to the forequarters. Pressure of the foot of an overangulated limb behind the body comes too late to produce the optimum 'drive'. Then again a rather straight limb with a not over-angulated hock and stifle, swings more naturally in pendulum fashion from the hip, and although it may not create as long a stride as the more highly angulated limb, it produces more strides per minute. The balance definitely lies in favour of the straighter limb. This applies particularly to sprinters, not only among horses but also in greyhounds. The smaller straight-limbed racing grey-hound can run away from the highly angulated exhibition type, although the latter do quite well in a long course in which initial speed is not essential.

A well developed brachiocephalic muscle is an essential, as this is one of the main muscles pulling the leg forwards. As it is attached at one end to the skull and neck vertebrae, and at the other to the humerus (Chart Three), its alternate contraction and relaxa-tion causes the head to jerk at each stride of the forelimbs. This action is noticeable at the trot when the forelegs are moving in opposite directions. However, as the foreleg on the other side of the horse is in action and moving in the opposite direction, both the rhomboideus and the cervical part of the serratus ventralis muscles are pulling on the neck in the opposite direction. These muscles counterbalance the swinging effect of the brachiocephalic, but only when the horse is fresh. As it tires the head is swung from side to side at each stride.

AND FASTER

The gaits so far examined, the walk, trot and rack, are all basically symmetrical ones, with an even spacing of the intervals between footfalls, and an even distribution of the moments of instability. However, the distinctive feature of the gallop is its lack of symmetry, with a single phase when all four feet are off the ground, and a partial synchronization of the two fore- and the two hindlimbs. During the gallop the horse executes a series of springs through the air, mainly as the outcome of rapid contractions of the hindlimb retractor muscles, and the extensors of the individual limb joints. The hindfeet are driven violently against the ground during the later phase of the stride. The horse never has more than two feet on the ground at any one moment and usually only one.

The normal order in which the feet are moved during the gallop is:

LF   RF   LH   RH

—alternatively the sequence may be:

RF   LF   RH   LH

At all speeds the period of suspension occurs after the second forelimb footfall. The body is projected off the ground by a powerful upthrust of the front foot. This push-up is necessary for the recovery of equilibrium particularly in a fast, heavy horse without a flexible spine. In an animal such as the greyhound, the hindlimbs can be brought right under the body without the strong upthrust of the forelimbs because of the supple vertebral column (Fig. 42 in the Appendix).

The closer together the hindfeet contact the ground the more efficiently do they act as a propulsive unit, but the shorter their period of support of the body. To counteract this the stride between the two front feet is close to the maximum possible in order to prolong the support phase of these two limbs for the greatest possible linear distance.

A galloping horse may carry a hindfoot as far forwards as its own umbilicus beneath the centre of the abdomen, and a forefoot as far forward as a line dropped perpendicularly from the muzzle. The foot however, does not contact the ground until retraction is well under way, i.e. until the limb axis is nearly vertical. The actual impulse provided by the foot does not take effect until the body has passed over the vertical limb and the toe of the foot is brought into play. The limb is lifted off the ground soon after the vertical has been passed. The complete range of protraction and retraction relative to the hip or shoulder is much greater than in the walk, but the actual 'step' is much shorter.

The flat foot is necessary for support and to hold the ground while the body passes over it by means of its own momentum, but it plays little part in facilitating the speed at which the body moves through the air, until the body has passed over the limb's dead centre. It is at this moment that the driving power of the limb can begin to be utilized. The horse propels its body not only by its hindfeet during the gallop but also by its forefeet, making use of the contraction of the flexor muscles and tendons at the hind part of the limb which drive the toes into and push against the earth. The forefoot usually lands on the heel, the weight of the body then passes to the wall, the quarters and finally to the toe of the foot which is forced by the weight upon it either against hard ground, or slightly into soft ground, actually pushing against it, thus further aiding the forward propulsion of the body. A hindfoot on the other hand, is more inclined to thrash backward at the ground and in galloping the toe seldom digs into the ground until the limb has reached the perpendicular. In fast galloping very little other than the toe of the hindfoot comes into contact with the ground. It will be seen from this that moderately firm going increases the efficiency of performance and that the peculiarities of an animal's gait, dependent partly upon its conformation, may decide whether a horse is a mudlark or gallops best 'on top of the ground'.

The canter is more or less a slow gallop. In the gallop there is an alternation between both frontfeet and both hindfeet, whereas in the canter the lateral support phase is still in evidence, and the first front footfall tends to coincide with the last hind footfall.

At the walk, trot and rack, the two rearlegs are always moving in opposite directions, the croup swings from side to side slightly on the sacroiliac joints, but up and down lumbosacral flexion is practically non-existent. The side to side swing of the croup adds slightly to the length of the stride, for at each step by the hindfeet the hip is swung to that side. In the gallop the spine can be flexed slightly in the vertical plane to bring the hindlegs further forwards at the beginning of the stride. After having said this we must recall that the rigidity of the horse's spine has been mentioned and compared with the suppleness of the spine of the racing greyhound. In the horse the body is of use in locomotion mainly as a medium for the accommodation of muscles and is so much dead weight which has to be transported. However, limited flexibility occurs at the gallop as the hindlimbs are brought forwards and the croup is flexed around the lumbosacral articulation by the contraction of the hip flexors (psoas major and iliacus). This contraction is accompanied by the reciprocal relaxation of the longissimus dorsi and the medial gluteal (running from the sacrum and ilium to the major trochanter of the femur). When the foot contacts the ground the lumbosacral curve flattens by the action of the body weight and contraction of the longissimus dorsi and medial gluteal muscles. The psoas major and iliacus muscles 'give' absorbing energy and storing it as potential energy of displacement. As the back straightens the lower end of the femur is pulled backwards by the passive lifting of the back of the pelvis as a complement to the contraction of the biceps femoris muscle.

It is to be emphasized that lumbosacral flexion is of very limited importance in the horse, and the muscles mentioned in the lumbo-sacral region of the spine are mainly concerned in a cooperative antagonism between those which lie above the spine and those which lie below the spine. This is carried out with the object of preventing the spine from bending both horizontally and vertic-ally. The horse's spine is in fact rigid enough so that any force which would cause it to bend more than a little might easily result in a broken back. This often happens when a tumble or some unusual struggling occurs. It is also not an infrequent occurrence when casting a horse for operation. Most spinal fractures in the horse occur in the thoracic region as stated in Part One. The limited degree of movement in the spine of the horse takes place between the last thoracic and first lumbar bones, between the first three lumbar vertebrae, and between the last lumbar vertebra and the sacrum.

The length of the strides of a galloping horse have been estimated fairly accurately of late years by exponents of show jumping in the setting and spacing of jumps. This can be based only on a knowledge of the average number of strides taken between succeeding obstacles. A racehorse at full gallop, judging from the distance between the prints of the same foot in the earth, can be shown to cover as much as 25 feet with each impulse of the hindlimbs. This involves propelling roughly a cylinder weighing 10 cwt., a distance of 25 feet through the air. However, since the body at the time of the jump has usually established a considerable momentum, the amount of muscular effort required is much less than if the body were simply 'dead weight'.

During the gallop the head and neck undergo some oscillation. The downswing requires very little muscular action, the ligamentum nuchae is so arranged that its pull practically equalizes the weight of the head and neck, when held in the normal rest position. From here only a slight amount of energy is required to either raise or lower it. Therefore at the gallop when the foreleg hits the ground the head and neck swing down around the articulation of the last neck with the first thoracic vertebra, through a passive swing brought about by normal gravitational force. This movement alters the relationships of certain muscles to the scapula. The rhomboideus and the cervical part of the serratus ventralis now have a more acute angle of insertion onto the scapula. The smaller the angle of insertion, and thus the angle of application of power of a muscle on a bone, the greater the stabilizing effect exerted on that bone. Therefore as the leg contacts the ground the scapula moves down and back as it accepts body weight, and the head swings down. Both actions increase the stabilizing effect of the two muscles mentioned above during the part of the stride when the main function of the limb is support of the body weight rather than propulsion. At the end of the stride the springing of the forelimb lifts the centre of gravity and the head and neck swing upwards by the elastic rebound of the ligamentum nuchae.

A LIMIT TO SPEED

When the horse is moving along at a steady speed the main job that the limbs are performing is the same as when the horse is at a standstill, namely to support the body against the pull of gravity. The forward propulsive thrust of the limbs is quite small and the absolute speed of movement depends on the frequency of operation of the limbs. As previously mentioned, it is necessary if a horse is to increase its speed that the hindlimbs shall travel backwards faster than the forward speed of the body at that moment. Therefore the retractor muscles must develop more power, implying that these muscles are working below maximum when the horse is moving slowly. Similarly it will be necessary for the forelimbs to move forward sufficiently fast to synchronize with the greater rapidity of movement established by the hindlimbs. Therefore as speed rises the duration of both retraction and protraction decreases, but retraction decreases more so. The rate of stride is increasing and the speed of limb muscle contraction is increasing, but the speed at which a muscle can contract is limited, and thus the velocity of the action it mediates is also limited. Simply enlarging the muscle, or doubling up the number of muscles, will increase the power available but will not increase the speed of action. Speed is increased by altering the relative lengths of the lever arms being operated by the muscles, and by decreasing the length of the power lever arm. Thus throughout horse evolution there has been a trend towards increased length of limb, and shortening of many limb muscles so that they attach close to the hip or shoulder joints (the pivots of motion), to increase the swinging speed of the leg and foot. These short muscles, such as the middle gluteal and part of the adductor muscle mass in the hindlimb, retract the limb rapidly but with relatively little power. Similarly, protraction is brought about by short muscles such as the psoas major, iliacus and superficial gluteal in the hindlimb, again having little power but high speed. The horse however, retains sufficient long axis, high power muscles, such as the biceps femoris and semitendinosus of the hindlimb, for bringing about acceleration from a standstill and moving at slower speeds.

The speed of the leg can also be increased if, at the same time, different muscles extend different leg joints in the same direction. The overall propulsive effort, represented by movement of the foot, will exceed the motion produced by any one muscle working alone. The individual speeds of each limb segment combine additively to give an absolutely higher speed. We have therefore the raison d'etre of the limb being used as a propulsive lever rotating by extrinsic musculature from the hip or shoulder, and the limb being used as an extensible strut by intrinsic muscle action extending each individual joint.

Maximum speed is reached when both sets of muscles, extrinsic and intrinsic, are exerting their maximum power output, and thus the duration of both protractor and retractor phases of movement is at a minimum.

Speed can only be maintained for as long as the momentum of the body can be kept slightly on the increase, since growing muscle fatigue is liable to tire the limbs until they are no longer able to move faster than the body. The tendency is then for the momentum to fall to the extent that the limbs are no longer able to re-establish it. The horse which comes up to win in the last few yards is one which has reserved enough of its energy to make its limbs move faster than the speed of the body at the moment of making the effort.

COMING TO A HALT

A limb whose axis is extended in front of the vertical exerts a backwardly directed horizontal force on the body which acts as a brake. The time at which the limb imparts forward momentum to the body depends on the limb having passed the vertical and having relinquished its weight carrying role. During a complete stride a limb acts alternately as a brake and a means of active propulsion, with a period overlapping both when weight is being supported.

Braking depends upon the use of the heels of the fore- and hind-feet with dorsiflexion of the foot enabling the toes to be raised. In the hindlimbs also, hock and stifle flexion gently employed throws more body weight onto the hindfeet, which are kept as nearly as possible beneath the belly rather than striding out behind the body. A horse during the trot or gallop cannot pull up immediately as it can during the slow walk, so that when pulling up it will have to reverse the gait by which it broke into the trot or gallop and finally pull up from the walk. This is why after a race it takes time to bring a horse to the halt, as it has to reduce speed slowly, through trot and walk, before finally coming to a standstill.

JUMPING

Although the downward thrust of the hindfeet against the ground is an important factor in galloping it is even more so in connection with jumping. During galloping the impact of the toe of the hindfoot with the ground does not require force so much as speed, as the greatest part of the propulsion takes place during the last third of the backward thrust. Whether a horse accelerates or retards depends upon whether the speed of limb movement is greater or less than the momentum of the body at the time. In addition, each impact of the hindfoot with the ground produces a braking effect, since when the foot lands on the ground at a spot lying below the horse's umbilicus there is a slowdown while the body travels over the foot. This is accomplished by virtue of, an at the cost of, its own momentum, before the foot reaches the situation where it can begin to make use of the power lying behind it.

When jumping, the amount of power or drive required from the hindlimbs depends to a large extent upon the speed at which the jump is approached, the momentum of the moving body at the time and whether the position of the feet at the moment of take off is calculated to permit the hindlimbs to make their full effort. A clever horse, a clever rider, and someone equally clever at the laying out of a course and placing the jumps, may make it possible for the horse to arrive at a jump without changing step, altering its stride, or actually charging into the obstacle.

Preparation for the jump begins when the body is supported by the leading foreleg. The front part of the body must now be lifted from the ground and the centre of gravity moved back along the body. Thus the head and neck have their advantages for the experienced jumper uses these to alter its centre of gravity in order that the weight of the body may concentrate at whichever part of the body it is most needed. The forehand is pushed into the air by the straightening of the forelimb. The shoulder and elbow extend through the action of the short heads of the triceps on the elbow joint, and the biceps brachii and supraspinatus muscles on the shoulder joint. Especially important is fetlock extension, through the superficial digital flexor, but mainly through the more muscular deep digital flexor. The serratus ventralis muscles also contract to shift the centre of gravity backwards but also to lift the body in relation to the scapula, which is itself rising because of the shoulder extension. The anterior deep pectoral muscle functions here together with the serratus muscle. The epaxial musculature of the back between the croup and the neck also contracts strongly, arching the back as much as is possible in the horse, and helps to raise the front end of the body.

At the same time as the forehand is being raised the hindlegs are being brought together beneath the body to support the weight. There is practically no period of suspension between the lifting of the forelimb and the placing of the first hindfoot. The take-off by the hindlegs occurs close to the foot print left by the leading foreleg. Then, rising to the occasion, the horse straightens the hindlimbs by extension of stifles and hocks and also fetlocks and hips. The last named joint is extended by the action of the biceps femoris, semitendinosus and semimembranosus muscles aided by the middle gluteal muscles inserting onto the major trochanter, and the posterior parts of both adductor and gracilis muscles which pass onto the shaft of the femur. The last three muscles, because of their shorter lever arms, are not powerful muscles but muscles of speed. The former group of muscles comprising the bulk of the quarters are inserted lower down the leg and have a longer lever arm, being more powerful muscles but imparting less speed. We have a situation whereby the movement is started by the long lever arm muscles, which also provide the strength of pull, but the rapidity of the movement occurs after limb straightening has been started and inertia lessened. This latter action is brought about by the short lever arm muscles.

The muscles of the quarters also serve directly to extend the stifle and hock joints through the patellar insertion and the tarsal tendon onto the tuber calcis. Stifle joint extension is added to dramatically by contraction of the three vastus muscles of the quadriceps femoris group. These extend from the front of the femur, the rectus femoris muscle of the group also crosses the hip joint so that during this action the rectus femoris component is contracting to regulate the smooth extension of the hip joint. Hock joint extension is supplemented greatly by the gastrocnemius muscle, and the reciprocal mechanism of tendo-ligaments supplements all of the muscles in opening out these two joints. The final impetus to the jump is given by fetlock straightening, mainly through the action of the deep digital flexor muscle.

The moment the forefoot leaves the ground the forelimbs begin to flex, especially at elbow and knee. These movements are aided by brachiocephalic contraction bringing the forelimb upwards and forwards. Thus at the moment of take-off the forelegs will be bent up together and the hindlegs will be fully extended. The force employed has to lift the belly clear of the top bar, when its own momentum, coupled with the force of gravity, should complete the jump, except in double and triple bar events when the lift has to be greater in order that an increased momentum may carry the body a little farther before gravity causes it to descend.

When the horse makes its great effort, driving the feet hard against the ground in order to suddenly straighten its hips, stifles, hocks and fetlocks, the upper parts of the limbs, the quarters, thighs and second thighs, will be travelling much faster than the parts of the limbs from the hocks down, because the feet will be planted firmly on the ground until they are actually lifted by the moving body. This effect of lifting the hindfeet may even exert a retarding influence, which is best understood when we remember that a man jumps better in light shoes than in heavy boots.

The practised jumper will flex the hocks and stifles in order to bring the feet safely over, or it may kick out behind in order to extend these joints behind the body, mainly through the gastrocnemius muscle and the action of the reciprocal mechanism. At the same time as the hocks are flexing the forelimbs are extending preparatory to contact with the ground. Contact is made with one extended foreleg followed closely by its fellow which is placed out in front of the first to give a good base of support. The second forefoot impacting allows the first to be moved out of the way quickly since it is in the place where the hindfeet will come to earth. The hindlegs come down one after the other, but before the second has touched the ground the foreleg has already pushed off.

The strain upon the joints when a horse lands first on one foot then on the other, as it should do, is very heavy especially as practically the whole weight of the horse plus the influence of gravity as the horse descends from a height (gaining momentum

on the way down) falls on one foot. Frequently the fetlock comes
to the ground, and if, as sometimes happens, the horse lands on
its heel (having advanced the forelimb a little too far) and the toe
turns upwards, the strain exerted upon the navicular bone by the
deep flexor tendon as it passes over it may easily damage the
tendon or cause fracture of the bone. When landing in this
position, the forefoot having reached the ground too far ahead
of the body, or if it has skidded forwards on slippery turf, there is
no hope of the body using it as the spoke of a wheel and passing
over it. Nothing is left except for the other forefoot to make a
rapid advance. In a good many instances when the forefoot
skids in this fashion, particularly during a hurdle race, the body
sinks in front and the second forelimb is unable to straighten
out. Instead it doubles up at the knee and the horse falls.

Horses were presumably not originally designed as jumpers,
as evidenced by the relative rigidity of the spine. The fore-end
of the body is heavy, with a heavy head suspended at the end of
a long neck, all of which tends to bring the animal back to earth
as soon as it has risen to its maximum height, except on the less
frequent occasions in which momentum, the timing of the run-up
and the take-off are all perfect. In order to be a good jumper a
horse needs long but not heavy limbs and a body which is slim,
light and streamlined. It needs also to be lightly built at the front
end and strongly built at the rear. Although a horse does not profit
as a jumper by carrying heavy shoulders, too heavy a head or
too wide a front, it certainly helps if it has a well laid back shoulder
with sound forelimbs and feet.

PART FOUR

SOME THOUGHTS ABOUT CONFORMATION

The days when horses were regarded seriously as a practical means of road transport have disappeared for ever. In any large city, nowadays, the only horses to be seen belong either to the mounted police, or to the local brewery, or on rare occasions to a local hawker who finds a horse-drawn vehicle convenient for his door-to-door transactions.

In more congenial surroundings we are left with some hunters and a children's riding school, sometimes a combination of the two, racehorses and a few point-to-point aspirants, an apparently unlimited stock of children's ponies of every type and description, and here and there some polo ponies. Trotting ponies came and began to diminish in numbers, but there seems to be a prospect that trotting matches may again increase in popularity.

Outside the show ring and the gymkhana there seems little room at present for the hack except in wide, open spaces, which are becoming fewer; and with rare exceptions the farmer has forsaken the horse excepting in certain counties where tractors get bogged-down or are unable to ascend mountains.

But in spite of all the handicaps the sale of live horseflesh remains big business, and racing stock, moorland ponies and the miniature thoroughbreds which pass as children's ponies are costing more money than ever before. While buyers at an auction sale are prepared (as happened recently) to pay out an average sum of £140 for unbroken ponies, off a hilltop, there is little fear that the supply will cease.

All this may seem to have little connection with the title of this chapter, other than to enable its writer to draw attention to the fact that good conformation has a market value, even if it has yet to be shown whether appearance and ability will run hand in hand. There are, of course, occasions when such a question appears to be of little importance. Horses, especially young stock, are judged on their looks; by what they should be capable of doing, but in many instances have never attempted. It might be interesting to determine the proportion of hunters winning regularly in the showring which have ever jumped a gate, or followed hounds with serious intent; or how many, having retired from the show ring, are purchased by hard-riding thrusters, or by seasoned riders seeking the perfect mount?

It is the purpose of such animals to impress upon breeders the features of conformation which *should* provide material capable of being trained and educated to perform a particular kind of work. Well-shaped young animals have a greater market value than plain ones, but it is unfortunate that choosing a horse by its looks is nearly as great a gamble as selecting a wife with an eye to her vital statistics. Good hunters, like good racehorses, come in all shapes and sizes. Even a gymkhana pony lacking a single visible good point may run rings around those which arrive in expensive horse boxes accompanied by their grooms.

The truth is that there is virtue in a great many horses, as in a great many people, utterly unassociated with good looks or even with physical perfection, which enables them on occasion to confound their critics. Whether it is sheer pluck, determination or the will to win is hard to decide. One experienced trainer is quoted as remarking that many horses won races because their hearts were superior to their hoofs. This might be taken either literally or metaphorically with equal truth. What such a statement really means is that although good conformation is very desirable, and while a horse possessing it should be better equipped to stand the strains and stress of work than its ugly brother, it is essential that it shall also possess the right kind of temperament, one which enables it to fall in with the requirements of its rider and to battle to the last breath even against more seasoned performers.

A horse possessing perfect conformation, good manners and ability equal to its appearance is a joy to own, or even behold, but the sad truth is that a great many plain horses are useful and willing performers, while almost as many of those better favoured in the matter of conformation are not.

Let us briefly consider the main features of conformation which might be expected to have a definite value.

If one is choosing a horse for personal use, the first feature to consider, although it cannot be regarded as conformation, is *expression*. Probably no animal, man included, offers a better indication of its temperament and reliability than the horse; at least to those capable of interpreting it. There are no poker faces in the horse world. Its expression, constantly changing, is an open book, portraying its emotions, moods and temperament, as well as the rapidity of its reflexes.

The horse one would buy is a sensitive animal, never lethargic but very much alive, registering vitality. It possesses features which convey expression. Firstly the eyes, then the ears, the nostrils, sometimes the voice: the lips, the skin covering the face, the quick movements of the head upon the neck, the character of the respiration, the display of temper, or the whimper of welcome.

Now, coming down to more mundane matters, one should take note of the head and compare it with the length and substance of the neck. A heavy head goes better with a short strong neck, while a light head will need a longer and slimly built neck to make the best use of it. As the head and neck are very important parts of the machinery which effects the distribution of weight throughout the body, constantly altering the position of the horse's centre of gravity, the type of head and neck should be correctly related to the general body weight, particularly in cases where the horse has an extra good forehand, the body being markedly heavier in front than behind, as in such a case the weight regulating influence of the head and neck is particularly important.

That portion of the neck situated immediately above the jugular furrow contains the brachiocephalic muscle running down the whole length of the neck and overlying the cervical vertebrae at its lower end, where they produce prominences very hard to the touch. This muscle is easily distinguishable and the degree of its development will provide a very good indication of the horse's bodily condition and general fitness, as well as of the strength with which it can advance its forelimb.

It is interesting to realize that however pleasant it may be to watch a hack, a hunter or a saddle pony taking a long front stride, its foot skimming neatly over the ground, and following this up with a neatly extended hock and hindfoot brought softly to earth at the right fraction of the second, the actual length of the stride (granting its aesthetic virtues) makes little, if any, actual difference to the rate of progression.

The reason is that when the front foot lands slightly farther forward than usual it is also farther from the shoulder than if the stride were shorter. It therefore takes slightly longer for the body to travel over the foot that rests on the ground than when the front stride is shorter. Accordingly the hindlimb has to wait a little; it must move forward a little less rapidly in order to permit the forefoot to complete its elongated forward stride. The actual number of strides per minute is correspondingly reduced, although each stride may carry the body a little further over the ground.

So far as speed is concerned, it is a question whether a smaller number of longer strides cover the ground more quickly than a greater number of shorter strides, and the impression one gets from extensive observation is that while a longer stride looks better, gives a better ride and is more pleasing in every way, the short quick stride is the more effective.

Relating to this is the fact that less than a century ago there existed in south-west England, and probably elsewhere, a breed or strain of 'running ponies'. These were mainly of Dartmoor descent and probably crossed while on the moors with some gipsy's stallion in the first place. They were characterized by the remarkable shortness of their strides during the fast trot. Their forelimbs rarely extended beyond an angle of 25 degrees with the ground in front of or behind the shoulder joint, and the hindlimbs took similarly short strides to match the front action. The hocks and stifles were almost perpendicular. But although their action was grotesque their limbs moved so quickly backward and forward that they developed a speed with which no ordinary pony could compete. Some of these ponies persisted for a good many years, even up to the commencement of the First World War, when they were frequently driven in the Cornish miner's 'shays', but they disappeared when tin-mining came to a halt. To ride one of these ponies in a trotting race was quite an experience. The stride was too short and rapid to enable one to 'bump saddle' and one could decide between riding stiff-legged in cavalry style or humping oneself upon the pony's withers, which was the approved method in Cornwall long before the advent of Tod Sloan.

Continuing our inspection, one should take note of the jugular furrow and observe whether there is any sign of a 'jugular pulse', a regular impulse running up the jugular vein. When this exists it is due not to a regurgitation of blood from the heart, but to some slight check upon the entrance of blood as it flows back into the heart, which causes the jugular vein to become distended from below upwards. This pulsation becomes more evident when the head is held down, as when the horse is grazing, but in most instances it is evident when the head is held normally. When it persists unduly after pulling up from a short canter, it may be regarded as advisable to seek professional advice.

Standing in front of the horse, one notes the width between the points of the shoulders and between the forelimbs at the level of the elbows. If you will take a glance at Fig. 43 in the Appendix, you will see that the thorax of the horse is suspended in a cradle of muscles and that the greater the amount of chest and muscle lying between the two scapulae the greater must be the width of the chest. This is particularly evident when the first few pairs of ribs are widely hooped, giving rise to a slightly barrel-shaped chest. The ideal is fairly straight ribs until the fourth pair, after which they should be deep and well curved, carried well back to near the stifle, so as to avoid a 'slack middle'. It is not easy to find ribs so obliging in this respect.

Other causes of a wide chest are a too well developed sternum, often in company with an upright shoulder. The more inclined the scapula is, the farther back are the muscles which cover its outer surface, so one gets a streamlined effect. Overloaded shoulders usually go with an upright scapula. Streamlining is of great importance in every horse required to gallop. This applies also to the manner in which the neck is set into the shoulders. Although a little fullness in front of the shoulder may have its advantages in the case of a harness horse, it certainly has none in one required to race.

The carriage of the head needs considering as well as the set-on of the head upon the neck. A good guide is to estimate the amount of space between the wing of the atlas and the hinder edge of the lower jawbone. This should be wide enough to accommodate two fingers, increasing to three at the lower angle of the jaw, between this and the jugular furrow. When the head is set-on too closely, the space available for free breathing at this point may be constricted, with the risk of pressure upon the larynx, especially when the horse is close-reined.

One must recognize the kind of back that provides a good seating for the saddle, comfortable for the horse as well as for the rider. High withers are an asset provided they are suitably clothed on either side with muscle, do not stand up as a ridge, but taper away gently from above to below, providing a wide surface which will prevent the saddle sinking down until the rigid arch of the pommel presses upon the spinous processes which form the upper edge of the withers. This will not only cause the horse pain and cramp its action, but also it may lead to bone necrosis and the development of a fistulous wither.

The back of a horse should be sufficiently wide to give the padded portion of the saddle comfortable support, but not so rounded as to permit it to turn around the horse's body whenever one tries to mount by putting weight on the stirrup. Nor should the rear end of the thorax be sufficiently narrow to allow the saddle to slide backwards.

As has previously been mentioned, the elbows of the horse may vary in their position in different individuals. In many race-horses they are set far forward, almost directly below the shoulder joints. This type of formation usually goes with an inclined scapula and a short humerus. The angle between the humerus and radius generally remains fairly constant, but the length of the humerus is subject to a good deal of variation and such variations may be transmitted genetically. Limbs set well forward may tip the horse on to its toes, and help quick starting.

In horses engaged in sprint races this type of conformation may have advantages, but in jumpers it may well interfere with balance; older horses are inclined to go 'over at the knees' but, curiously, in thoroughbreds this does not appear to carry the same risks as it does in half-bred stock. Many good winners have been this way from birth.

In contrast to the above, some horses have their elbows set far back under the body. This depends upon extra length of the humerus, and conformation of this type not infrequently goes with upright shoulders. The optimum position of the elbows and withers ensures that the horse's girths reach forward to an inch behind the point of the elbow. Elbows set back a long way increase the amount of concussion transmitted, not only to the spine of the horse but also to that of its rider. Any departure from the optimum position of the elbows will throw extra strain upon the hocks, which have to perform additional work to compensate for discrepancies in forelimb action.

As previously mentioned, ribs should not be too wide beneath the girths, but should be carried well back along the body with some additional spring behind the saddle. This type of chest, narrow in front and expanding as it passes back, provides a good respiratory capacity, with the additional advantages that it permits streamlining at the front end of the horse and also provides a more comfortable seat in the saddle.

The forelimbs will be close together, or wide apart, according to the space taken up between the two scapulae. They incline to be close together when the elbows lie in the forward position and to be wide apart when the elbows are situated farther back under the body. Once again, the happy medium is desirable. The forelimbs must be perpendicular from elbow to fetlock when viewed from any position, followed by a sloping pastern compatible with the weight and type of horse. Feet must look straight ahead, being neither turned in at the toe nor pointed outwards. There should be no knuckling at the knees or fetlocks, and the tendons behind the cannon bone should be firm and clear cut, without being thickened or bowed.

This is the moment to take a good look at the horse's forearms and also its second thighs. The great importance of adequate development of these parts of the body has already been stressed. Standing behind the horse, the two pin bones (angles of the haunch) should be level and must match perfectly. The thighs between the hindlegs should almost touch, being rounded and full. A cut-up appearance, with a lot of daylight between the thighs, is a sign either of debility or of lack of muscle. The hindlimbs must be parallel from stifles to feet. A plumb-line dropped from the seat bones should pass straight down the back of each hock and down the hinder edge of each cannon. If the stifle and hock are abnormally angulated (bent), the cord will pass down the side of the cannon bone or in front of it. If the hindlimb is abnormally straight, the line will pass slightly behind the hinder edge of the flexor tendons, behind the cannon bone.

It must never be forgotten that a horse, a perfect picture at the standstill, may be far less attractive when set in motion. View your horse from the back, the front and the side at its various paces, and standing off at a convenient distance, never too close, determine whether the limbs are carried in a straight line with the body, whether the feet keep company with the limbs, turn in (pin toe) or outwards, whether the horse dishes, and even the manner in which the feet land upon the ground. Remember when viewing a horse going away from you that if it flexes its fore- and hindlimbs as it should you should be able to see the sole of each foot at some portion of every stride.

When the horse is coming towards you, note whether the stifles remain in line with the body or if they are 'punched' outward as they flex. In this case the hocks will probably turn inward. From the side of the horse in motion, look out carefully for level hock action. The point of each hock should rise during flexion to exactly the same height. If one is slightly lower than the other, it may be spavined. If one is carried a good deal higher than the other and with a jerk, stringhalt may be present. These observations will need confirming by a professional opinion.

Note carefully the amount of wear of the shoes of each pair of feet and especially whether the toe of one hind shoe is much more worn than that of its fellow. In this case watch that limb again in action and make sure there is normal flexion of the hock joint.

After you have done all these things, make sure your horse can go into reverse by having it backed.

APPENDIX

The conclusion of this book is made up of a selection from a series of articles contributed by the author to *Horse and Hound* during 1965. It has been requested by a number of readers that these should be included, and, as they have a considerable bearing upon the subject-matter of the present volume, we have agreed to do so, with the full permission of the Editor of *Horse and Hound*.

It must be accepted that the articles submitted may at times repeat or enlarge upon, some of the material in the text of this book, but it is hoped that they will present it in a manner which will make the subjects discussed more easy to understand.

THE HORSE AND HOW IT WORKS

Before one can understand how a horse accomplishes all the feats demanded of it, and before one can appreciate the complicated mechanism which lies behind all its varied activities, it is necessary to have some idea as to how the horse is constructed, how the various parts of its body work in harmony and to realize some of the disabilities with which different parts of the body have to contend. The horse has been with us a long time and those among us who grew up with it were apt to accept it as a part of our normal existence and make very little attempt to discover why and how it ticked. It is unfortunate perhaps, but true, that active research into equine matters on truly scientific lines only commenced at the time when the horse threatened to become extinct. Today, the veterinary profession, as well as the intelligent horseowner, has a far greater knowledge of the horse, its physiology and dynamics, than ever before, and it is partly on account of this newly acquired knowledge that we may expect it to remain with us for a long while to come. Before acquiring this necessary understanding of the horse and its behaviour it is essential to overhaul and revise all one's long-held and ingrained theories, forget a great many of them, and begin to regard it as a piece of elaborate machinery conditioned by human agencies to carry out a great number of extraordinary activities for which it was never designed; a robot in many ways, but a robot equipped also with a mind of its own and a considerable degree of independence.

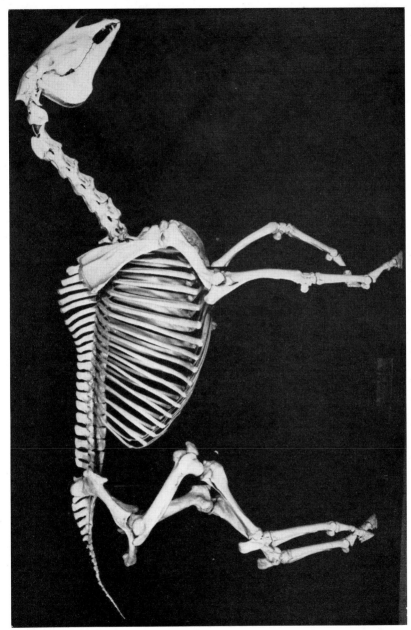

Plate 2. Skeleton of Foxhunter (1940–1959) in the Anatomy Department of the Royal Veterinary College, London.

There appears to be a commonly accepted belief among those who know a good deal about horses, as well as those who know nothing, that the horse was constructed as (and has always been) a natural jumper, possessed of a flexible and supple body and capable of maintaining its balance, with complete synchronization of movement between the various parts of its body, at all paces and all available speeds. The truth which has to be faced and duly allowed for is that the horse is provided with an almost rigid and inflexible carcass of considerable bulk and weight, and that this has to be propelled solely by the use of the limbs, over the ground and through the air, as so much ballast. Apart from the fact that the trunk provides anchorage for the muscles which actuate limb movements, this heavy equine body becomes a serious handicap to the horse's rapid and flexible progression.

Briefly, the horse is made up from a head and neck, a trunk (thorax and abdomen combined), four limbs and a tail.

The head and neck may be regarded in two ways; first as a freely movable mass attached to an almost rigid body, designed in such a way that it enables its owner to focus its eyes and see a great deal which it would miss were its head less mobile; and secondly, the head itself acts as a heavy but adjustable bob-weight suspended upon the end of a long and extremely flexible lever, the neck. This ingenious mechanical arrangement permits the animal to alter its centre of gravity, or as some prefer to regard it, its centre of balance, at will. This plays an essential part in enabling the horse to overcome the difficulties attendant upon hurling the weight of its body safely through space or propelling it upon terra firma.

The thorax, which contains the heart and lungs, and the abdomen, containing the large and voluminous intestines and their contents, are extremely weighty—although extremely necessary to the horse—and are obliged to travel with it wherever it goes. This involves a considerable amount of air resistance, but the degree of streamlining compatible with lung and heart room varies a great deal in different individuals, and this may make all the difference between success and failure in a race, either on the flat or over hurdles. For all practical purposes the thorax and abdomen may be regarded as the fixed and unalterable section of a projectile, which is lifted into the air and propelled through space or just above ground level by means of the combined efforts of the fore- and hindlimbs working in harmony.

Having passed through a long period of evolution, from the marsh-dwelling animal possessed of four or even five toes on each foot to the soliped travelling on dry, hard land, the modern horse is obliged to maintain the upright position, balanced (more or less) upon four props terminating in hard feet of small diameter, whose foothold is made even less secure by the fitting of narrow iron shoes. With the aid of such feet the horse is compelled to balance its entire body-weight on the flat, uphill, downhill and when landing from a jump and, moreover, it has to use them as brakes whenever it comes to a standstill or needs to slow its pace. Around corners at speed these shod hoofs have to work in perfect harmony, with dead accurate timing to maintain balance of the body and avoid spills, even in the absence of interference.

A close consideration of its mechanical features, and the problems it has to encounter in order to please humanity, should convince the majority of readers that anatomically the horse is quite unsuited to the performance of the tasks we set it. The majority will also rightly remain convinced that by virtue of stamina, determination, a genius for adaptability—and on account of some peculiar kink in its mentality—the horse succeeds in carrying out most of these tasks remarkably well.

MOVING A RIGID BODY

The horse's spine was designed originally to fit in with a very different way of living, environment and set of circumstances from that with which the modern horse has to cope.

Being an herbivorous animal with a voluminous intestine, the horse normally carries a large part of its body weight behind its midline. Although the chest capacity is of necessity large, the lungs within it are collapsible, inflatable and very sponge-like, and accordingly light in weight. The thorax itself, supported by thoracic vertebrae and comparatively light ribs, would be completely outweighed by the abdomen were it not for the help provided in maintaining balance by the presence of a long neck supporting a weighty head at its distal extremity. The abdomen is at all times loaded with partly digested vegetable matter, weighing seldom less than half a hundredweight and often a great deal more. After the limbs have been removed from the carcass the thorax and abdomen remain united to form a shuttle-shaped structure almost rigid in its length, incapable of being flexed (bent) to any marked degree in either direction. It follows, therefore, that the horse is compelled to propel this unyielding burden over the ground, or worse still, through the air over obstacles, without any help from its body, entirely by means of the energy created by the hindlimbs, the forelimbs being employed mainly to receive the weight of the body when it lands, and to keep the front end of the horse propped up until the hinder part is again able to take charge.

This is somewhat different from the conception existing in the minds of many horsemen, who regard the horse as being able to make full use of spinal flexibility during dressage operations.

The task of propelling an uncooperative body is made even less easy when the shoulders are wide and heavy and there is complete absence of any bodily streamlining.

Carnivorous animals, those which hunt the herbivore, all possess extremely flexible spines, which enable them to arch their backs almost into a semicircle, thus adding considerably to the potential length of the hindlimbs which, in these animals, are brought to the ground during galloping well in front of the forefeet. The greyhound, in common with the members of the cat family, is able to arch not only the lumbar but also the thoracic spine until the hindlimb, free for all practical purposes, plays the part of a pendulum swinging from the hip joint.

The length of the hind stride is also increased by the amazing degree of spinal flexion, which permits the hind-end of the body to descend nearly to ground level, thus enabling the whole length of the hindlimb to be utilized (Fig. 42).

Since the horse has an almost rigid spine incapable of any useful degree of flexion, and because the thigh is coupled with the body and held there by heavy muscular and ligamentous attachments, its femur (thigh bone) has also only a limited degree of movement contrary to what has usually been asserted in textbooks regarding its range of flexion and extension. Although many horses can lash out behind

FIG. 42. The gallop in the greyhound and horse showing the greater degree of spinal flexion possible in the former.

and even carry the hocks behind them over a jump, the forward range of movement, which is what counts in propelling the body onwards, is so slight that even at full gallop the hindfeet of the horse do not meet the ground farther forward than a line dropped perpendicularly from the animal's navel. This is why so few horses can 'cow-kick' in a forward direction, while the ass, mule and zebra use this kick as one of their main weapons of defence.

In the horse family a ligament, the accessory, unites the lower front portion of the pelvis to the head of the femur and this alone would be sufficient to limit femur movement, even if the nature of the horse's upper thigh permitted it, which it does not.

The horse gallops, therefore, by obtaining most of its advancement of the hindlimb through the stifle joint.

During the gallop the weight of the body falls on either the fore or hind pairs of feet, with intervals during which it falls upon only one foot at a time. During one phase of the gallop—and quite frequently in some horses during a fast trot—all the feet are simultaneously off the ground for a fraction of a second.

Apart from the great difference between horse and greyhound in other respects, especially spinal flexibility, the greyhound owns a femur much less closely united to the rest of the body than is the case in the horse. This permits the greyhound to enjoy freedom of thigh movement throughout the greater part of its length.

The surprising thing about the horse is that, handicapped as it is by an almost complete absence of spinal flexibility as well as by a limited range of femur movement, it is still able by employing the hindlimbs (and to a lesser extent the fore) as propelling organs, with the head and neck to preserve balance, to hoist a bulky, heavy and unhelpful body over obstacles as formidable as the Aintree jumps.

To provide better understanding of the lack of flexibility present in the spine of the horse one should first consider the vertebral column as a whole and then assess the degree of movement possible in its individual sections. In the horse, as in all other vertebrates, the spine must be regarded as the keypin of the whole bodily structure. Upon it is hung all the principal factors connected with locomotion (as well as the all-important head), and it would be true to say that the type, conformation and way of living of every vertebrate animal is dependent upon the shape, character and degree of mobility of its vertebral column.

If one could be sure of breeding the perfect spine one could be equally certain of breeding the perfect horse.

Unfortunately, however, the horse's spine was designed originally to fit in with a different way of living, environment and set of circumstances from that with which the modern horse has to cope in order that it may retain its relationship with mankind. If such a relationship should weather another million years it is just possible that the spine then being produced may be entirely suitable for tasks comparable with those of today, enabling a horse to compete at 2 years old in sprint races, later try its luck at longer distances and eventually, perhaps, be relegated to jumping and asked to race for anything up to four miles over a formidable course.

The comparatively short time which man and horse have yet been together has been quite insufficient for the necessary evolutionary changes to have crept in. That the horse succeeds as well as it does is attributable to its pluck and the breeding into the modern thoroughbred of that wonderful quality which, for want of a better understanding, we term 'stamina'. *It is not because it is admirably fitted physically to succeed.*

SWINGING IN A CRADLE

When we speak of balance as it applies to a horse in motion we have a mental picture of its body continuously supported in safe equilibrium by the four limbs at whatever pace the horse is travelling, whether it be moving over the ground or being propelled through the air.

A pony bending as it gallops between sticks is quite unable to curve its body throughout its length when taking a sharp turn. How, then, does it maintain balance?

Safe equilibrium implies that the body is at no time in danger of overbalancing in any direction sufficiently to interfere with efficient performance, even when the body is tilted over to one or other side, as it may well be when the horse is negotiating a curve at speed. It is also highly important that the body shall be controlled by synchronization of the movements of the limbs, the head and neck and thorax, in such a way that during its passage along the curve it will not swerve out of its direct course as the result of centrifugal force. The body, perfectly balanced, will permit uninterrupted use of all the limbs in order that the foot pertaining to any one of them may be planted at the horse's will upon the exact spot calculated to provide the best possible support to the moving body.

It is the unbalanced horse which swerves away from the straight course and throws its perfectly balanced neighbour completely out of its stride.

This is one type of balance. A slight variation in pattern may be seen when a horse is cantering easily along the flat, where there is no likelihood of collision or interference and the animal has unhampered control of its head and neck, as well as of its tail. The principle operating then is that the front half of the body *swings in its thoracic sling* (Fig. 43), in perfect rhythm with the movements of the forelimbs. The hinder end of the body follows the lead given by the front half after the manner of a dancing partner, the hindlimbs extending and flexing either one at a time or simultaneously, moving the centre of gravity slightly forward or a little to the rear, in an easy effort to hold the body either upright or at an appropriate angle longitudinally, as well as horizontally in relation to the ground surface.

What do we mean when we say that the body swings in its thoracic sling? *First note very carefully that the thorax of the horse is not attached to any part of the forelimbs by any form of bony or rigid union. It is suspended between the two shoulder blades, cradled within a sling made up of muscles.*

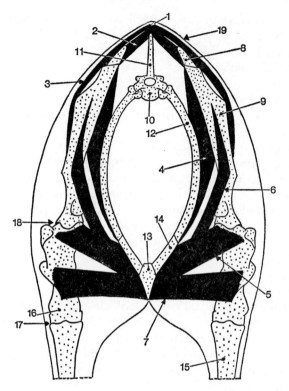

FIG. 43. Diagrammatic section through the chest at the level of the scapula. The thorax is suspended between the fore limbs entirely by muscular attachments and not by bone. This enables the rib-cage to move within its cradle of muscles and, as the thoracic spine is an almost rigid column, the body of the horse moves with it.
(1) Withers.   (2) Thoracic part of rhomboideus muscle.   (3) Trapezius muscle.
(4) Thoracic part of serratus ventralis muscle.   (5) Posterior deep pectoral muscle.
(6) Anterior deep pectoral muscle.   (7) Superficial pectoral muscle.   (8) Cartilage of prolongation of the scapula.   (9) Scapula.   (10) Body of thoracic vertebra.   (11) Spinous process of thoracic vertebra.   (12) Rib.   (13) Sternum.   (14) Costal cartilage.
(15) Radius.   (16) Humerus.   (17) Elbow joint.   (18) Shoulder joint.   (19) Body surface.

The thorax has thus a great deal of lateral movement. Also, it can be lifted very slightly within its seating, or allowed similarly to descend within it whenever it is necessary to keep the centre of gravity low.

At any time when the body is safely balanced upon the feet either of the forelimbs can be abducted, that is to say it can be drawn away from the ribs and the walls of the thorax. This is a very important observation and it plays a very active part in dressage movements, as well as in the horse's everyday movements.

A pony 'bending' as it gallops between sticks set in the ground is quite unable to curve its body laterally throughout its length when it takes a sharp turn. Instead, it *adducts* a forelimb, the one on the side nearer the stick, and *abducts* the opposite limb. If, let us say, the horse pulls the left forelimb in closer to the thorax, the body can actually roll over slightly towards the left within the thoracic sling. The horse will then reverse the procedure in order to circumnavigate the next stick, the body rolling towards the right side in accordance with the siting of the stick.

In a rather lesser fashion this is precisely what happens when a racehorse gallops at speed around Tattenham Corner. Its body does not actually bend, as many think it does, but it rolls in its cradle while the horse is negotiating the bend, with its innermost limb tucked closely in alongside its ribs and the outermost taking a slightly wider sweep than it would otherwise do. When the horse is turning a corner in this way one might suppose that the innermost limb must slow down and the outer increase its speed. What really happens is that the two limbs move at almost the same speed, but the outer takes a slightly longer stride.

Owing to the cradling of the thorax in its muscle sling a horse is able to move both forwards and sideways at the same time, and it is this freedom of abduction and adduction of the forelimb in relation to the chest wall which plays so important a part in certain dressage movements. The ability to move the body in two directions at the same time has sometimes erroneously been attributed to an ability on the part of the horse to bend the body laterally.

Nevertheless, not every horse is able to carry out such movements and at the same time maintain perfect balance without loss of speed, even after efforts at training. The balance regulating mechanism is based upon what is known as the horse's proprioceptive sense. This provides the animal with information which enables it to decide whether its body is right side up, upside down or in some ways off its balance. This proprioceptive sense is closely associated with the horse's internal ear and its semicircular canals. It seems probable that the degree of development of this sense is a genetic legacy handed down from ancestors—something which the horse either has or has not!

The 'Cutting Horses' possess this sense and utilize it to perfection.

A 14-hands pony may be able to execute a figure-of-eight during a hand canter, without checking, in less than four body lengths, making use of the thoracic sling, hock flexion and pivoting upon the hindfeet; the body remaining rigid during the whole movement.

The head and neck not only decide the direction in which the body shall travel, but they also help to maintain equilibrium by calculated disposal of their weight.

In order to maintain perfect balance at all gaits it is important that the horse's limbs shall be sound and straight—and particularly that the feet shall be level and correctly shod. The forefeet should slope at the right angle with the ground beneath, neither too upright nor too flat, while the frogs should make positive contact with the ground beneath them. The four points of connection between the horse and the ground upon which it operates cover a very small total area, and ability of the feet to put on the brakes, release them in order to slow down or accelerate, is vital if balance and stability are to be maintained. With this in mind, the importance of depth of heel and properly maintained frog pressure cannot be stressed too highly.

THE VITAL HOCK

Most important of all the joints in the horse's locomotory system, the hock is also hardest worked.

We have already considered concussion as it affects the front end of the body. Let us now take a look at the hinder part and also at the body itself. The hindlimbs of the horse absorb concussion, too, although in the normal course of events they do not suffer the same degree of road shock as the forelimbs.

Stifle and hock work in coordination, not individually. When the horse bends (flexes) its stifle, the hock flexes simultaneously; when it straightens the hock, the stifle also straightens; the one cannot function without the other. A horse straight in hock is also straight in stifle, and one that has a much bent stifle will probably carry its hocks behind a line dropped perpendicularly from the seat bone.

Practically the whole of the concussion travelling up a hindlimb is counteracted automatically by means of combined hock and stifle flexion. This operation is modulated and controlled by means of two opposing sets of muscles working in complete harmony.

These are firstly the hamstring muscles which pass down the hinder part of the thigh and are attached below, with the gastrocnemius and superficial digital flexor of the second thigh, to the summit of the tuber calcis of the hock by means of the Achilles tendon. Secondly the quadriceps femoris muscle mass and the tensor fasciae latae of the thigh, together with the tibialis anterior and the tendinous peroneus tertius of the second thigh. The tendinous peroneus tertius acts as a stop to prevent the hock overstraightening itself into a double-jointed state.

The first set of muscles straightens (extends) the hock; the second set bends (flexes) it (Figs. 44, 45). By the cooperation of this pair, both contracting together with one assuming dominance, the hock and stifle contrive to bend and straighten slowly, rapidly, or even in mid-air without undue jerking or strain. This muscular arrangement in the hindlimb is on a par with that existing in the forelimb, where the biceps and triceps operate in a spirit of cooperative antagonism.

The fetlock and pastern of the hindlimb play their part in soaking up concussion, but as the hind pastern is less pliant than the fore and usually less lengthy, and the hindfoot more upright and narrower than the fore, they have not the same importance as in front, more especially as the hindfoot, when in operation in conjunction with the hock and stifle, needs to be planted squarely upon the ground. It may, however, need complete flexion when a horse leaves the ground during a jump, or it may require extension during braking movements when the heels are required to dig into and slide through the turf beneath them.

The hindlimb, unlike the fore, is articulated to the skeleton at the hip joint and pelvis. Concussion is transmitted through the pelvis directly along the spinal column, being partly absorbed by the intervertebral discs, especially in the lumbar region.

Of all the joints in the locomotory system of the horse, the hock is the most important—and it is also the hardest worked joint in the body. Viewed as a piece of machinery, it is an outstanding specimen of work.

It combines two kinds of joint. One is capable of free but directional movement; the other is almost purely devoted to shock absorption. If the machine has a weakness, it is in this latter structure that it lies. It was never designed for work on hard roads or on cinder tracks, but for use in the marshes and on the grassy plains, for which the construction was ideal. When man changed the horse's environment, he failed to modify the machine to fit the new conditions.

The hock joint of the horse comprises an oblique, gliding surface, grooved to resemble a pulley. This rests between the lower end of the tibia and the double row of smaller, flattened bones which make up the second, anti-concussion, part of the whole structure. Behind this pulley-like bone, which is known as the tibial tarsal, there is anchored by ligaments another irregularly shaped bone which carries a four-inch lever, to which is attached the gastrocnemius, superficial digital flexor, biceps femoris and semitendinosus muscles. This lever-like projection is known as the tuber calcis.

There is very little movement between these flattened bones, either as rows or individually. The tibial tarsal, the bone which carries the pulley-like, gliding surface, is furnished with a deep central groove and two lateral raised and rounded ridges. The groove winds with a spiral twist downwards, forwards and outwards, taking almost half a turn around the bone (Fig. 44). The lower end of the tibia is moulded to fit accurately into this groove and adjust itself to its ridges, so that in pulley fashion the joint can work smoothly and handle great weights with a minimum degree of muscular effort. Additional leverage provided by the tuber calcis greatly adds to the efficacy of the joint, giving much greater power to the muscles, the tendons of which are attached to its summit.

In mounted warfare not so long ago efforts were made by one's adversary to hamstring one's horse by slashing through the Achilles

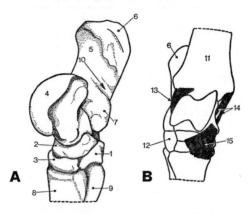

FIG. 44. Hock joint of the right side.
A. Medial view. B. Anterior view showing the main ligaments of the hock.
(1) Fused first and second tarsals. (2) Central tarsal. (3) Third tarsal. (4) Tibial tarsal. (5) Fibular tarsal. (6) Tuber calcis. (7) Sustentaculum tali. (8) Third metatarsal. (9) Second metatarsal. (10) Tarsal groove for flexor tendon. (11) Tibia. (12) Fourth tarsal. (13) Short lateral ligament. (14) Short medial ligaments. (15) Dorsal ligaments.

tendon with a sword—which goes to show that these warriors had some knowledge of equine dynamics.

It is rare to encounter cases in which the pulley-like surface of the tibial tarsal, or its cartilage, has sustained any extensive damage or ulceration, although bog spavin may result from faulty conformation, often hereditary in origin; the increase in the quantity of synovial fluid within the joint may sometimes act as a safety valve by lessening the amount of friction between the joint surfaces.

Even a bog spavin of considerable size may frequently be unattended by any considerable degree of lameness.

Most of the ulceration of the joint surfaces, associated with wear and tear of the greatly abused hock, occurs between the two lower rows of flattened bones which lie under the tibial tarsal, between it and the upper end of the cannon bone and the lesser splint bones. This ulceration gives rise to true bony spavin.

The other portion of this compound pulley which operates in conjunction with the muscles of the hindlimb lies in the joint between the femur and tibia and between the femur and the patella. This is really a compound joint, being made up of these two sections, which communicate through their synovial sheaths and work together in co-operation.

The joint between the patella and the grooved portion of the femur (known as the trochlea), exists in the limb solely to enable the tendon of the quadriceps femoris muscles, which straighten (extend) the stifle, to glide over the front of the stifle joint without friction. The patella may almost be regarded as a bony appendage of the muscle, shaped in such a way that it enables the quadriceps femoris muscle to exert the maximum degree of leverage over the joint—see Fig. 45.

The stifle joint of the horse has its equivalent in the human knee and it suffers from similar disabilities in the way of cartilage damage, luxations and inflammatory changes. In some cases the cause is strain or overwork of the joint, but in far more instances it is due to hereditary unsoundness resulting in abnormal shaping of the joint.

Whether or not a stifle or a hock is likely to give efficient service will depend upon the following factors:

(a) The straightness or degree of flexion of the stifle and hock joints, as judged with the animal standing squarely.

(b) The degree of obliquity or straightness of the ridges and grooves in both the femoral trochlea and the tibial tarsal trochlea of the hock.

(c) The condition of the synovial membrane lining of the joint.

(d) The age at which the colt or filly is first called upon to perform strenuous work.

Horses possessing rather straight hocks and stifles are usually faster in a sprint than those with longer tibial bones and greater angulation of the hocks and stifles, because greater speed results from a larger number of short strides than from a lesser number of longer strides during the same period of time. But the straighter stifles are more liable to suffer from luxation of the patella, especially during the period of growth between two and three years.

One famous stallion, noted for its straight hocks and stifles, produced a great many colts and fillies which suffered from this form of stifle lameness during their adolescence, but usually lost it after the fourth year. Other stallions sired by this horse handed down the same defect.

In addition to straightness of the stifle and its potential dangers, some slight defect in the shaping, or in the degree of obliquity, of the grooves and ridges of both the trochlea of the femur and those of the tibial tarsal within the hock joint, may interfere slightly with the act of flexion. This loss of smoothness may not be evident until the animal is put to work, when the defect becomes obvious to the horse, which then adapts itself by developing some abnormal style of gait, handling the limb in an awkward manner or assuming an abnormal stance while at rest. This is another example of a hereditary defect.

In other cases either the trochlea of the femur or the joint shaping of the tibial tarsal may be apparently normal, but the pair do not completely match, so that the cooperation between the pair is imperfect.

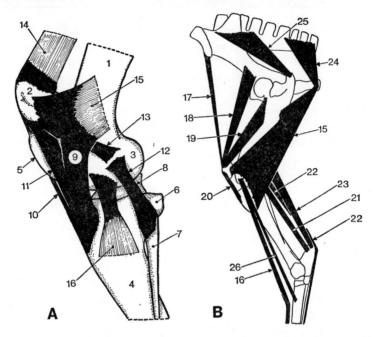

FIG. 45. A. Stifle joint of the left side in lateral view. B. Diagrammatic representation of the muscles operating stifle and hock.
(1) Femur.   (2) Patella.   (3) Lateral femoral condyle.   (4) Tibia.   (5) Medial trochlear ridge.   (6) Lateral tibial condyle.   (7) Fibula.   (8) Lateral meniscus. (9) Lateral patellar ligament. (10) Medial patellar ligament. (11) Middle patellar ligament. (12) Lateral femorotibial ligament. (13) Lateral femoropatellar ligament. (14) Quadriceps femoris muscle. (15) Biceps femoris muscle. (16) Long digital extensor tendon. (17) Tensor fasciae latae. (18) Rectus femoris muscle. (19) Vastus lateralis, medialis and intermedius muscles. (20) Patellar ligaments. (21) Tarsal tendon of the biceps femoris. (22) Superficial digital flexor. (23) Gastrocnemius muscle. (24) Semimembranosus muscle. (25) Middle gluteal muscle. (26) Peroneus tertius muscle.

In consequence of any of these hereditary defects undue strain is thrown upon the joint mechanism and particularly upon the lower rows of flattened hock bones, the purpose of which is to minimize strain or concussion falling upon any part of the joint mechanism. Once again, the end result is the development of bone spavin and possibly bog spavin as well.

When one studies the mechanism which operates the hock and stifle joints in unison one cannot fail to be impressed by the enormous amount of work carried out in antagonistic cooperation by the extensor and flexor muscles in securing perfect synchronization.

OCCUPATIONAL HAZARDS

Operating in a way of life for which it was never designed, it is not surprising that the mechanism of the modern horse is often subject to breakdown.

Like other working machinery, the mechanism which activates the horse has its weak spots. It is probable that for use in the marshes and on the plains, the terrain amid which the horse developed, the existing machinery was quite efficient. Since then the horse has altered in shape a great deal and in performance considerably more, being now con-confronted with an environment and a way of life for which the old machinery was never designed. In consequence breakdown is not infrequent.

The damage resulting from concussion may arise suddenly, but more often it develops slowly but steadily. The harder the ground underfoot, the greater is its effect. Anti-concussion measures, outlined in the previous article, are fairly effective under normal conditions, though not infallible. They were designed to operate during normal gaits and I have pointed out already that during its natural existence—while an occasional sprint might become necessary—persistent fast galloping over several miles was never a part of the horse's programme. *Nor was jumping, except occasionally in case of emergency.*

Unfortunately, some of the more serious injuries which may cause a breakdown in the machinery occur not when the horse is operating on firm ground but when it is wholly, or almost wholly, suspended in mid-air.

We have already observed that galloping necessitates the synchronization of groups of opposing muscles and that any momentary interference with the timing may result in the shattering—and the word must be taken literally—of even the heaviest bones in the body, simply because they are unable to withstand the uncontrolled, opposing pull of two sets of muscles a little out of harmony. In similar fashion the cast horse, with legs or feet pinned against the ground, a wall or a partition, may as the result of violent unsynchronized limb movements, sustain fractures in the spinal vertebrae, or in the limb bones themselves, quite unassociated with direct traumatic injury.

The greyhound can smash a limb in mid-air in precisely the same way but it will seldom break its back, simply because the dog's spine is very flexible, unlike that of the horse; and when a greyhound does develop a back injury it is more often a disc displacement than a bone fracture, brought about by the fact that, owing to its extreme flexibility, the spine has curled up like a Catherine-wheel.

A horse, falling over a hurdle or other type of obstacle, may land on its poll, or with the neck actually folded upon itself. In such instances the bones of the neck are liable to fracture, or the horse, striking its poll heavily, may fracture some of the bones at the base of the skull. On other occasions a horse may lose control of its coordination when high above a jump, duck its head and land upon the summit of its withers, with the result that the rigid body and its hindquarters somersault over the head, which is now somewhere upon the ground. In order that such a performance may be carried out without serious injury to the horse it would be necessary for the spine to yield throughout its length. *As this is quite impossible in the horse, it is likely that the thoracic bones may fracture.*

When a horse sustains damage when landing from a jump upon its feet the injury more frequently involves the foot, bones of the pastern, the fetlock, or some of the tendons or ligaments at the back of the cannon. Fracture of the bones of the coronet and pastern may arise from plain concussion, but it also occurs during the act of getting away from the landing place after a jump, whenever a foot receives a sudden check.

In this country where made-up tracks are not in common use, fracture of the third phalanx is comparatively rare, but pedal ostitis, inflammation of the bone of the foot, is comparatively common.

The navicular (distal sesamoid) bone, and its relationship to the third phalanx and the deep flexor tendon, is probably the weakest spot in the machinery of every horse required to jump and gallop (Fig. 46).

The sesamoid bones at the back of the fetlock and the navicular bone within the closed hoof are called upon to provide two lubricated pulley surfaces over which the powerful, ever busy, deep flexor tendon must glide during every movement of the foot and lower limb. Had Nature realized to what use the horse would eventually be put, it is certain she would have provided a couple of very much larger and stronger bearing surfaces, better related to the rest of the machine. Even if she had thought the proximal sesamoid sheath capable, she would have made some extensive alterations to that of the navicular bone.

The two flexor tendons, superficial and deep, pass down the back of the cannon. The superficial tendon terminates at its insertion into the second phalanx, the bone of the coronet above the third phalanx, by means of a bifid tendon. Through the loop thus formed, the deep tendon passes to continue beneath the skin of the heel, entering the foot, gliding over the navicular bone and becoming finally attached

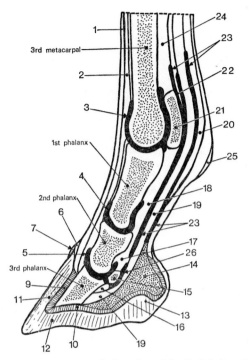

FIG. 46. Diagrammatic vertical section of the limb below the knee.
(1) Skin. (2) Common digital extensor tendon. (3) Capsule of fetlock joint. (4) Capsule of pastern joint. (5) Capsule of coffin joint. (6) Corium of periople. (7) Periople. (8) Coronary corium. (9) Laminar corium. (10) Corium of sole. (11) Wall. (12) Sole. (13) Frog. (14) Digital cushion. (15) Navicular bone. (16) Distal ligament of navicular bone. (17) Suspensory ligament of navicular. (18) Inferior sesamoidean ligament. (19) Deep digital flexor tendon. (20) Superficial digital flexor tendon. (21) Proximal sesamoid bone. (22) Ring formed from superficial flexor tendon. (23) Digital synovial sheath. (24) Suspensory ligament. (25) Ergot. (26) Navicular bursa.

to the sole of the pedal bone. Figs. 46 and 47 should make this clear.

While the horse is standing erect the pressure upon the navicular bone is practically nil, but it may become very severe whenever the horse lands upon one foot, as it must do, and particularly so whenever the first foot to come to earth is advanced well in front of the body, as happens when a hurdle is cleared at speed.

In very soft going, when the heels are unable to exert their normal braking action and the foot slides along the ground with the fetlock trailing on the ground surface, as in Fig. 48, the risk of navicular fracture becomes accentuated, and this is particularly so whenever the navicular bone is already affected with disease and has become porous, or when the composition of the bone is deficient.

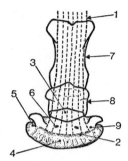

FIG. 47. Bones of the undersurface of the foot showing the passage of the deep flexor tendon over the navicular bone.
(1) Deep flexor tendon. (2) Semilunar crest for tendon attachment. (3) Navicular bone. (4) Sole surface of third phalanx. (5) Angle. (6) Volar foramen. (7) First phalanx. (8) Second phalanx. (9) Third phalanx.

So far we have made no reference to the strain thrown upon the flexor tendons at the back of the lower limb, whenever the foot, pastern and/or fetlock assume any of the awkward positions shown in Fig. 48.

The superficial tendon extends downward only a short way below the fetlock before being inserted into the second phalanx but the deep tendon, as previously mentioned, carries on into the foot. This deep tendon is reinforced by the check ligament, which is a flat fibrous band arising from the tissues covering the back of the knee, to become inserted into the lower part of the deep tendon at about the middle of the cannon bone.

Both the check ligament and the deep flexor tendon may become strained simultaneously or, if the strain is mild, only the check ligament may suffer. The superficial tendon may become involved also, and in horses which suffer easily from tendon trouble the two tendons may

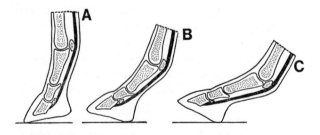

FIG. 48. Diagrammatic vertical sections of the foot bones, showing the effect of the pull of the deep flexor tendon as it passes over the proximal sesamoid bones and the navicular bone.

develop adhesions through a healing together of their surrounding tissues.

The end result, as most owners know only too well, is contraction of the tendons, with usually some form of knuckling, dependent upon the tendons involved.

Behind the check ligament lies a somewhat clastic, flattened band of considerable strength, the suspensory ligament, which is attached to the upper ends of the sesamoid bones. This is designed to prevent over-extension of the fetlock joint, and in ordinary circumstances it would undoubtedly act as a very efficient preventive of tendon strain.

The time when this combination of tendons and ligaments may fail to operate efficiently is when synchronization of the movements between the fore- and hindlimbs momentarily fails while the horse is in rapid motion, and also during jumping whenever the hindlimbs are hindered in their return to the ground. In such a moment the first forefoot may descend safely, but the second straddles forward in an attempt to avoid a somersault, and this is the leg which receives the strain and is suscep-tible to injury. In normal jumping at moderate speeds, when the first foot reaches the ground almost perpendicularly with locked elbow and the other forefoot takes its measured pace just ahead of it, there is little risk of mishap. The speed at which jumps are taken today and the crowding of horses at any particular fence raises a number of problems never anticipated when the horse was first designed.

A GLANCE AT THE FOUNDATIONS

In view of its great importance let us again consider the horse's foot. To do it full justice would require a complete volume—and then much might remain unwritten. There is an old and very true saying: 'No foot, no horse.'

The four feet of a hunter capable of carrying 12 stone cover a total area of approximately 92 square inches of ground. Sometimes only one foot is making contact with the ground, at others two or three. It would be reasonable to estimate that any one foot out of the four may be called upon to support from 2–2½ cwt. while the horse is proceeding, mounted, at walking pace. As much as 8–10 cwt. may be supported by one forefoot, momentarily, when a horse lands from a jump carrying a rider. These figures are subject to considerable variation according to the height and weight of any particular horse, but may serve as a basis for calculation.

Size of the feet varies a great deal in different types of horse. Small, rounded feet are usual in thoroughbreds—with often a tendency to low heels. Large and flatter feet are seen in heavy breeds. Clydesdales have the largest feet, with rounded soles, often a little flat and wide open at the heels. Suffolks and Percherons have rather smaller feet than the Shires, which are usually rather more upright and very serviceable.

The foot is hardest and more enduring in native ponies—very suitable to animals living all the year outdoors and often on a meagre diet. Moorland ponies kept indoors and overfed on corn develop laminitis.

Most of these ponies possess rather small, upright feet, with an inclination of 55–60 degrees in comparison with 45–50 in the thoroughbred and half-bred horses. A characteristic of native pony feet is their high, upright heels, together with the hardness of the horn.

The wall of the foot is developed by a frequently irregular downward growth of horn secreted by the cells of the coronary band. Sometimes termed the coronary cushion, this is a ring of modified skin, covered with papillae, which in turn carry cells capable of secreting horn. Above the coronary cushion is a narrow groove separating it from a somewhat similar but smaller cushion known as the perioplic ring. This secretes a layer of a waterproof varnish which is intended to creep down and cover the wall of the foot, in order to prevent loss of moisture with an accompanying shrinking of the hoof and hardening of the wall. The

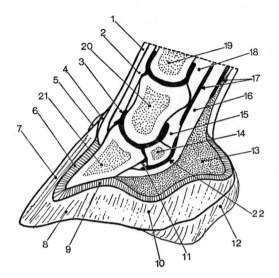

FIG. 49. Diagrammatic vertical section of the bones, tendons and hoof structures below the fetlock.

(1) Skin. (2) Common digital extensor tendon. (3) Capsule of coffin joint. (4) Corium of periople. (5) Periople. (6) Laminar corium. (7) Wall. (8) Sole. (9) Corium of sole. (10) Frog. (11) Distal ligament of navicular bone. (12) Heel. (13) Digital cushion. (14) Navicular bone. (15) Suspensory ligament of navicular bone. (16) Deep flexor tendon. (17) Digital synovial sheath. (18) Inferior sesamoidean ligament. (19) First phalanx. (20) Second phalanx. (21) Third phalanx. (22) Navicular bursa.

periople is usually rasped off by the smith for appearance' sake (Fig. 49). The rate of secretion from the coronary band permits the complete replacement of the horny wall in a period of from 8 to 10 months. When the rate of growth is irregular (intermittent), alternating ridges and circular depressions encircle the wall.

The influence of seasonal diet also produces rings. When the horn growth is accelerated, as when the horse is out on spring grass, raised 'grass rings' are produced. When horses rough it in winter, out of doors, depressions in circular form may appear later. Deeper and rather wider circular grooves may follow an attack of laminitis.

From a careful examination of the wall of the foot it may be possible to deduce the circumstances attending the horse's career during the preceding ten or twelve months.

In a correctly shod foot the weight of the body falls upon the wall of the foot and the frog, which should be permitted to make contact with the ground at shoe level. When only the wall receives the weight, the buffering effect of the digital cushion, the large pad of fibrous tissue which overlies the frog and fills a considerable portion of the hoof cavity, is completely lost, so that the concussion transmitted from the ground surface travels without interruption up the limb until partly absorbed by the pastern, a resulting stress being thrown upon the tendons behind the cannon bone.

At the heel the horny wall bends sharply forwards and inwards in the shape of a 'V' to meet the hinder end of the frog (Fig. 50). In this way the inturned wall forms an upright partition of horn and this, in company with the upright wall of the heel, constitutes the 'bar' of

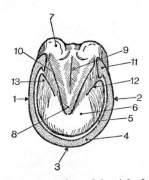

FIG. 50. Undersurface of the right forefoot.
(1) Thin wall.   (2) Thick wall.   (3) Toe.   (4) Wall.   (5) White line.   (6) Sole.
(7) Heel.   (8) Apex of frog.   (9) Central groove of frog.   (10) Lateral groove of frog.
(11) Angle of wall.   (12) Bar.   (13) Seat of corn.

that particular side of the foot. The purpose of the bar is to take additional weight upon the heel, especially as every horse, except during the slow walk, lands upon the heels first, then upon the frog, and finally upon the toe, as the body travels over the area of ground occupied at the moment by the foot. On each occasion that this happens the frog should take the weight, force the angle of the bars open, and so turn them into a pair of wedges which will prevent the heels from caving in and contracting. Each time the bars are forced apart they lift the fibroelastic digital cushion lying above them and exert pressure upon the network of blood vessels contained within the horny casing of the foot. This helps to empty these veins of blood and drive it up into the leg, where it can be taken care of by the normal circulatory system of the limb.

Without this pumping action at each step the horse takes, the foot would become congested, the horse footsore and weary, and in certain cases laminitis might supervene.

The digital cushion extends upwards between the two lateral cartilages, one of which develops from the wing on each side of the rear end
of the third phalanx (Fig. 51). As it does so it forces these structures
apart. To some extent this overcomes the contraction which would
otherwise occur at the upper circumference of the horny wall at the
level of the coronary band each time the lower circumference widens
under ground pressure upon the wall of the foot.

One has to recollect that shoeing is apt to throw these natural functions of the foot sadly out of gear and this is particularly so when thick
heels, and/or quarter clips, lock the wall in a vice and not only prevent

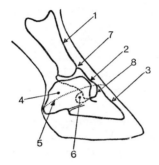

FIG. 51. Diagram to show the position of the lateral cartilage in relation to the
surface of the foot.
(1) First phalanx. (2) Second phalanx. (3) Third phalanx. (4) Lateral cartilage of
third phalanx. (5) Line of border of hoof. (6) Position of navicular bone. (7).
Pastern joint. (8) Coffin joint.

expansion and contraction but throw the pumping action exercised
by the frog out of action and set up venous congestion within the foot.

Nails, in themselves, exert a rather similar effect, but on a much
smaller scale.

It is a wonder that horses travel as well as they sometimes do, in
spite of the woeful interference with this so important part of the body,
exerted as apparently it must be owing to the hardness of modern road
surfaces and the fact that the foot of the horse is not what it was in the
days between the reigns of Richard I and Charles II, when the indigenous mares of this country were first introduced to Eastern sires. A
foot of a Welsh pony, running on the hills, may not be very impressive
at the first glance, but it fulfils its purpose admirably.

While three-quarters of the cases of lameness in shod horses may derive from
the foot, it is very rare to detect foot lameness in any of our indigenous ponies living
in their natural habitat.

The terminal bone of the foot, the third phalanx, is somewhat similar in shape to the hoof which contains it, but very much smaller. It is covered with soft, sensitive, fleshy laminae, which interleave with the horny laminae on the inner side of the wall of the foot. The toe of the third phalanx is somewhat chisel-like, in its formation and is directed downwards towards the sensitive laminae on the inner side of the sole of the foot.

When any undue weight falls upon the foot (as when landing from a jump), the tendency is for the toe of the pedal bone to descend slightly and exert undue pressure upon the sensitive sole. In its natural state, living in the marshes and on the plains, horses did not need to jump nor gallop on hard-baked racecourses.

It has even been suggested that this arrangement of the pedal bone within the foot was intended to prevent horses living in their natural state from attempting feats of agility beyond their normal ability.

According to modern statistics pedal ostitis has become one of the most common causes of chronic foot lameness in the horse. This is a disease which practitioners of fifty or more years ago did not record, not because they were any less observant than those of today, but because the condition did not commonly exist. This may have been partly due to the fact that hunters were seldom broken to saddle before they were 4 years old, race meetings were fewer and farther between, and 2-year-olds were not abused and misused as they are today. In other words the economics of horse-keeping have changed.